SEEK FOR A HERO

By

WILLIAM G. SCHOFIELD

The Story of John Boyle O'Reilly

P. J. Kenedy & Sons
New York

CS
1

To
MY FAMILY
For much loyalty and patience

*Where shall we seek for a hero, and
where shall we find a story?
Our laurels are wreathed for conquest, our
songs for completed glory.*

JOHN BOYLE O'REILLY

CONTENTS

AUTHOR'S NOTE

THERE ARE great men who live among us from time to time and who are too soon forgotten after death. John Boyle O'Reilly was such a man. He came to us as a hunted stranger, a condemned wanderer from another land. He stayed with us as an American for twenty years. He had much to tell us, for he had learned much. He learned as soldier, poet, fighter, editor, Irish patriot, British convict, Yankee sailor. And the greatest lesson he taught was the lesson of brotherhood and tolerance.

He brought new strength to the fight against bigotry and oppression, new force and integrity to American journalism, new enthusiasm to American democracy. It was our good fortune to have had him with us, though briefly; it was Ireland's misfortune to have lost him.

In writing this book, material has been obtained from O'Reilly's books, *Moondyne Joe* (P. J. Kenedy & Sons, New York) and *Athletics and Manly Sport* (Ticknor & Co., Boston). I have referred many times also to *John Boyle O'Reilly* by James Jeffrey Roche (Cassell Publishing Co., New York). Additional material has been obtained from Boston newspapers—the *Pilot, Herald, Traveler, Post, Globe, American, Advertiser*—and from the Catholic Encyclopedia, Encyclopedia Britannica, Encyclopedia Americana, and *Irish Quarterly*.

John Boyle O'Reilly was a man who should be remembered. This book is intended to help keep his name alive.

WILLIAM G. SCHOFIELD

I

VISION

(1844–1866)

They may talk of new causes! *Dhar Dhia!* our old one
Is fresher than ever today!
Like Erin's green sod that is steaming to God
The blood it has drunk in the fray.

From "Erin."

1. ROOTS

For JOHN BOYLE O'REILLY there was scarcely a day in his life when the fighting relaxed. One night, in his rich years as a Boston editor, he touched upon the reason for that. He did so, briefly, in the lines of one of his poems called "Distance." It read

> The world is large, when its weary
> leagues two loving hearts divide;
> But the world is small, when your
> enemy is loose on the other side.

Boyle O'Reilly's enemy was always loose. And whether it appeared as an individual or as a group or as a national sickness, it was always the same two-headed foe: Intolerance and Oppression.

It is not strange that O'Reilly chose to fight, for he came of a fighting line. He was Irish and he was a rebel, as his ancestors had been. It was born in him to challenge bigotry and tyranny.

It is not strange either that he managed to battle his way to America, and to carry on the fight from here with more vigor than ever. He realized early in life that his chances of winning were better in this land than in any other. And so he fought his way here from the other side of the world, from the cruelty of prison and the hot despair of a chain gang in the West Australian jungle.

He might have had a quiet, gentle life among the soft hills of Ireland. He would never have been content with that.

He was born at Soggarth on June 28, 1844. The town lay

some four miles above Drogheda and on the south side of the storied River Boyne. There stood the family home, ancient Dowth Castle, in one of the most beautiful valleys of a beautiful land.

The soil around him, there in County Meath, was rich with O'Reilly legend and stained in many a spot with O'Reilly blood. Going back a thousand years and more— even further back, to the Druids and the Milesians—the countryside had been the home of O'Reilly chiefs and princes, of warriors and scholars.

They had been there when the high kings of Ireland ruled with bright flags and bright courage on the Hill of Tara four miles to the west. They had been there on that Beltane Night —the pagan Night of Blackness—when St. Patrick led his little band of priests to the Hill of Slane, three miles to the north. And they had watched in awe on that night as the flames leaped out from Patrick's Easter fire, defying the laws of ignorance and superstition and wiping out the darkness that had spread across the land. The O'Reilly chiefs were there, too, when the Danes swept down from the north and conquered the land, and later, when the Normans came through. And they were there when Cromwell chose treachery above honor, and lured the people of the countryside into a trap that sprang shut with a bloody five-day massacre.

And when all the conquerors had come and gone, the name of O'Reilly still stayed on in the valley. And the sons of the O'Reilly line still were there to swim in the Boyne and wrestle and race on the soft meadow between Dowth Castle and the river.

Boyle O'Reilly lived there for his first eleven years. He was the second of three sons in a family of eight children. Poetry and song were always part of his childhood. His father, William David O'Reilly, was a brilliant scholar and a fine schoolmaster. His mother, Eliza Boyle, was equally talented, generous, and kind. The O'Reilly children probably learned more at the edge of the family turf fire and on walks and talks in the woodland along the river than ever they learned in the classrooms. And they learned much also of the history of their land and their valley, the rich and beautiful, tragic and desperate history of a people whose destiny seemed always to be conflict and trouble.

Those who knew him well said of Boyle O'Reilly that he loved many things in life, but among the things he loved best were a good song and a kind act and a fast and fair fight. They said that about him when he was a strong Irish boy, and when all he knew of the world was the valley of the Boyne and the harbor town of Drogheda, forever damp from the fog of the Irish Sea. They were saying it about him years later when he was a great American citizen with the tongue of a poet and the heart of a crusader. They were still saying it on a summer night in 1890, when he died at the age of forty-six in the little Massachusetts seashore town of Hull. And they were right all the way.

As a boy, he sang the songs of his parents and his grandparents and the land that hemmed them in. He sang all the songs that were sung in the valley between Slane and Tara, and when he had sung them all he made new ones of his own. They were sad songs of Irish heartache, and spirited songs of Irish battles, and bitter songs of Irish suffering. Those he made were like those he had known.

As a man, though, he sang for the world to hear, and not with his tongue but with his pen. He used it as a rallying trumpet. The words he sent forth told of the great teeming land that was America, and of how the Irish in their wretchedness should look to that land for hope and guidance. He had no patience with men who had lost the courage to fight.

He had no patience either with those who were blind to man's need for individual dignity. Long before he left Dowth Castle the dark-eyed and black-haired John knew well that an O'Reilly in Ireland had but one big choice to make in life: to join the long lines of the silent oppressed, or to join the desperate fight for his faith and his freedom—with his own neck at stake in the battle.

He was only eleven years old when he left Dowth Castle to get into that conflict. He was too young to fight with a gun or a sword, even if he could have found a leader to follow. But as young as he was, he had learned from his mother and father that words can be more devastating weapons than any iron armament in the arsenals of the world.

So, in 1855, off went young John Boyle O'Reilly to join the staff of the Drogheda *Argus* as a printer's apprentice. An enemy was "loose on the other side," and not at all aware of a new fighter entering the field.

2. PRINTER'S INK

SOMETIMES THERE, in the office of the *Argus*, Boyle O'Reilly daydreamed at his work. It was hard for a little boy to make the change so quickly, from trout stream to printer's ink, from green grass to hot lead. But it had seemed the thing to do.

It had seemed the thing to do, partly as a matter of family honor and partly for love of his mother, Eliza Boyle. Young William O'Reilly, almost three years older than John, had been bound out as a printer's apprentice at the *Argus*. That meant a firm two-way agreement: a working O'Reilly in exchange for a fifty-pound premium, paid to the family.

But Will stayed on the job only a few months before running into trouble. The work was too much for the boy, and he had to give it up or wreck his health. That was when John stepped in, partly to salvage the fifty-pound premium for his parents and partly to make good the family pledge that an O'Reilly would see the job through. It was his own gesture, made with as much thought as an eleven-year-old could put on the matter. And the family accepted the offer.

His starting salary was two shillings and sixpence a week —about fifty-two cents. The problem of board and lodging was his own, and no concern of the *Argus*. It was up to the family of a printer's devil to make up the difference between what he could afford for food and shelter and what he actually needed.

To hold his job, then, young Boyle O'Reilly had to be out of bed long before sunrise. The streets of Drogheda would be dark and lonesome, still wet with the dampness of night, as he trudged off to work. He would be on the job by six in the morning, and put in a solid three hours before taking an hour off for breakfast. Back on the job by ten, then a four-hour stretch before dinner. Back on the job at three in the afternoon, and then a five-hour stretch before it was time for supper. Usually he would be done with his work by eight o'clock at night, through with his supper by nine, and then get into bed as quickly as he could in order to store up a little rest.

There was not much time for daydreaming, but for an eleven-year-old boy there was always a moment here or there for looking back wistfully on the fun that was gone. He missed the river and the swimming, the woods and the walking, the murmur of the peat fire as the family gathered around the hearth of the old castle. He missed a boyhood that was too suddenly gone. He missed the storytelling of his mother and father. He missed the friendship of his dog, a little spaniel that had raced with him across the Boyne meadow and had sat with him on the riverbank, watching the fish. As he wrote about it a long time later:

> That little brown fat dog, that could not walk through the meadow, but had to jump over every tangled spot, and miss five times out of six, and fall and roll over when at last he succeeded, and have to be taken up then and carried—that little brown fat dog, with his flapping ears and hard belly, and straight short tail—who wore the hair off his back with lying on it to play with the big dogs, or with me; who never could trot, he was so fat and round; who always galloped or walked like an Australian horse; who was always so hungry that he never could take his milk quietly, but must gallop up to it, and charge into it, and make himself cough—the possession of that little brown spaniel puppy made me one of the happiest and proudest boys in Ireland.

Those things he missed, while trudging to work through the dark and foggy streets of Drogheda and while learning type faces and while eating cold potatoes for his supper. He was growing up much too early.

And yet Boyle O'Reilly was not unhappy. He liked his work, and the other workers liked him. And he found so many ways of doing extra jobs that before long he was earning twice his starting salary.

Then he began to think in earnest about Ireland. For the first time, and while still a boy, he began to feel some of the pangs that were racking his country. The office of the *Argus* was a good place to begin, for inevitably into the print shop came the material for political pamphlets and inflammatory handbills. And inevitably into any newspaper, no matter what its size, come the thinkers and the hecklers, the appeasers and the belligerents, the planners and the dreamers. And so they came to the *Argus*, where Boyle O'Reilly would take their hats in his ink-blotched hands and then listen to the visitors talk and argue while he was supposed to be at work.

He heard them speak of famine and death, of millions fleeing the land they loved, to seek a better life in some other part of the world. And he thought of how sad it was that any man or woman should have to go away from Ireland and never again see its crystal streams and its leaping salmon and its dark green hills. He heard them speak of past oppressions and past rebellions, and of the losers seeing their land snatched by the victors and of having to work like serfs on the soil they once owned. And he thought how unfair it was, that men should so treat other men. He thought how good it would be, if all men could love each other and live like brothers. He heard them talk of Ireland's humiliation, and of brave plans for putting an end to British control. And he puzzled for a long time over the reasons why one country should seek to dominate another.

Some of the things he heard were too complicated and too involved for him to understand. He didn't know enough about the world or about politics or about past rebellions to be able always to grasp Ireland's problem.

But there at the *Argus*—in the conversations and the back files and the reference books and the copy that was waiting to be set—there at the *Argus,* there still was much for Boyle O'Reilly to think about. He could understand the reasons for a shortage of priests, schoolteachers, Irish landowners, Irish merchants, even potatoes. And he could understand why Britain should want to make those shortages acute; he could understand that it is easy to control a land that's been beaten to its knees and stripped of its leaders and its food.

He did not always agree, though, with the way some of the discontented Irish looked at the picture. They spoke of their land as being in a state of slavery under British masters. He was only a boy, and so he could not fully grasp such things, but he remembered what his father had taught him back at Dowth Castle.

A slave master, his father had said, necessarily protects the life and health of his slave, if not through calculated kindness then at least through love of money. But this campaign against Ireland was a deliberate attempt to cut the population to a working minimum, rob it of its church, blind it with ignorance, and break its heart. His father had said that mere slavery was never the goal.

There in Drogheda young O'Reilly heard the story and tried to comprehend it. He read its history in books and pamphlets and newspaper records. And he kept it alive in the type that he set, and in his first awkward attempts to write poems and editorials. And he began to wonder if somewhere, at some distant time in his life, he might find a land where political and religious cruelties were not allowed—where there could be an understanding sympathy between a priest and a prison keeper, between a statesman and a soldier, between a landlord and a plowman, and among all men no matter how they were born.

At the *Argus* he would occasionally set type that told stories about the United States. He heard the men speak frequently of friends who had gone to America. He wondered if that might be the land where a person could lead such a life.

Then one day, when he was fifteen years old, the window shades at the *Argus* were drawn and a ribbon of black was placed at the door. The newspaper's owner was dead, and O'Reilly's work there was ended. Where would he go next in his search for the right way to live among men? It was too late to go back to boyhood play; already he was too tightly caught in the grip of questions and answers for that.

He had an English uncle, James Watkinson of Preston, skipper of a sailing vessel named the *Caledonian,* who sailed the Irish Sea, trading back and forth among the ports of England and Ireland. At about the time the *Argus* shut down, Captain Watkinson sailed up the gray channel of Drogheda Harbor to pick up a load of barley for his home town. And when the *Caledonian* cast off and shook out her sails again, Boyle O'Reilly was aboard, bound out for England and for a reporter's job on the Preston *Guardian.*

It was a pleasant time of life, that stay in Preston. In a sense, it was the last completely free and careless time he was to know. It lasted just short of four years, but its memories were still happy ones at the end of his days. As he said more than two decades later, writing from Boston to a friend in England:

It is pleasant to be remembered kindly through nearly twenty years of absence. To me every impression of Preston has kept its sharp outline. Yet I have been very busy and very unsettled during that time. But all the years and events fade when I think of dear old Preston—and I find myself on the River Ribble, in an outrigger, striking away under Walton Heights, or pulling a race between the bridges.

Do you remember the day we went to Ribchester, and then walked up along the river to Stonyhurst? Somehow that day stands out as one of the happiest and brightest in my life. I remember every incident as if it were yesterday. Though I lived only a few years in Preston, I love it and the friends I made there better than any I have since known.

In a worldly way I have prospered; and in literary repute I stand well in this country. I am busy from morning till night. But under all the changed appearances and surroundings, the stream of my old friendships and pleasures flows steadily along.

For a time, then—for the last time in his life, actually—he had several months that were tranquil and completely free of serious responsibility. He began to write light poetry that was much better than his earlier attempts at Drogheda. He took part in amateur theatricals, and in the town's traditional holiday pageants. He lived in the home of his aunt, Crissy Watkinson, on Deepdale Road. He read many books. And he became a part-time British soldier, by enlisting in Company Two, Eleventh Lancashire Rifle Volunteers.

It might have been a congenial way to spend the rest of his days, enjoying the easy life of Preston. But he was nagged by his own conscience, for he knew that life was far from easy in the land he had left. Thus, the more he read, and the more he heard in the barracks conversations of the Lancashire troops, the sharper became the realization that he could never turn his back on Ireland's tragedy. There was much work to be done there—his kind of work. Somehow, someday, a leader would come along who would make the country free. And perhaps, he thought, he, too, could help to get things ready for that day.

He was nineteen then, and it was March of 1863, when his father wrote to him and asked him to come back to his own land and find work on an Irish newspaper. Boyle O'Reilly knew what was in his father's mind. He had been expecting a call to come home. There was much to be done in Ireland and for Ireland, and only the Irish themselves could do it right.

If there was a tug at his heart on leaving Preston, there was a gladness and a challenge, too. At last, he knew, he was about to begin his real work. He'd had fun. Now it was time to get ready to fight.

3. FACTS AND FENIANS

IT WAS a late spring night in 1863 when young O'Reilly returned to Dowth Castle for a few short hours. It was a soft night, with the rain whispering gently against the ancient mossy stones of the castle wall. It was a quiet night, with no sound along the river valley but the occasional cry of an owl or the splashing leap of a hungry fish.

Inside by the hearth young Boyle O'Reilly sat with his parents and talked of the dreams of Ireland. His mother listened, thoughtful and proud, sitting with an unopened book of poetry in her lap. His father listened approvingly, sliding sensitive fingers up and down his watch chain. The others in the family had long since gone to bed. And Boyle O'Reilly drank his cup of tea and spoke of his hopes and plans.

He had changed considerably since the gray morning when he had left home to work for the Drogheda *Argus*. Then he had been barely eleven years old; now he was nineteen, with the spirit and restlessness of that age. Then he had been a careless boy, kicking at stones in the road; now he was a strong and imaginative youth—a youth with black hair, perfect teeth, clear eyes, broad shoulders, and quick fists. Also, he was a youth with a purpose in life; he was speaking of that now.

"It's a much bigger thing than Ireland herself," he said, "this disease of some men that makes them be cruel to other men. It's mankind's own sickness. It's not just England's— not just the sickness of one nation or one political group. It belongs to the world. But if we can cure it here in Ireland, we may help to cure it in other lands."

His father nodded agreement. "It may never be cured, but here's a good place to start trying. And that's why I asked you to come home from Preston—to work from inside—to be part of Ireland and help fight the terrible thing that walks our roads and tramples our fields. The place for you now, son, it's with a fighting newspaper in Dublin, where you can say what you like for all to read and hear."

"You have one in mind?" O'Reilly said.

His father and mother glanced at each other.

"I think so," his father replied. "They say James Stephens is starting a Dublin paper. He's naming it *The Irish People.*"

"Stephens the Fenian?"

The father nodded. "He wants a new voice of rebellion. He's planning something big."

The room was quiet, while Boyle O'Reilly let his mind center on what it would be like to work with the Fenians. For one thing, it would be dangerous. The movement was growing with astonishing speed; when it grew too strong, inevitably the British would move to strike it down. But meanwhile it might accomplish considerable good for the Irish people. He'd thought about that, even before returning from Preston.

The movement had been born in Paris fifteen years earlier, put together by a group of Irish political exiles. Its purpose was to tie together an international brotherhood of Irishmen who would work for a single purpose—to break the British rule and establish Irish independence. It took its name from the legend of Finn MacCumhail and his band of Fianna, a great tale in Ireland fully a hundred years before the coming of St. Patrick. And it chose for its model the Jacobin movement of the French Revolution, with all its fire and its zeal and its resentments. That was Fenianism.

O'Reilly knew some of the Fenians' ways. He had been

hearing of them since he was a boy, first at his own hearthside and later in Drogheda. He was one of them at heart. He acknowledged that fact, as he sat now and thought about James Stephens.

Once born, the Fenian movement had spread easily to countries all around the world, wherever an Irishman dreamed of returning home to a free land. O'Reilly had heard stories of its strength in America, in Italy, and even in England itself. And he knew something of what Stephens had done with it at home.

O'Reilly considered Stephens to be part despot but all patriot. He was a Kilkenny man who had been battling for Ireland's freedom almost since his birth thirty-nine years earlier. He had been wounded in the fighting at Ballingarry, in the daring but blundering uprising of 1848. A sorry thing, O'Reilly thought now—an uprising that had held no weapon except enthusiasm, and that had ended in bitter humiliation for the rebels. Still, he wondered—had it truly been wasted? Was any blow against oppression ever a waste? He didn't think so.

Stephens had been there, in the 1848 fighting. And five years later the Fenians had reached out from Paris and had tapped him for their chief organizer in Ireland. O'Reilly had heard how he had put together a group called the Irish Revolutionary Brotherhood, and how swiftly it had spread—from city to crossroads, from cottage to castle, from tavern to hideaway. And plotting at its head was Stephens, bitter and brave and tireless, a man of many disguises who had infuriated the British by his skill at standing in their midst and yet keeping out of their hands. And now he was starting a newspaper, to stir the dream of rebellion through Dublin.

But Boyle O'Reilly shook his head and put his empty cup on the stone floor. "No, Father. On a paper like that I'd write

my story just once and be in chains the next morning. I'd do
no good for anyone that way."

"What way, then?" The schoolmaster waited. "You've a
plan of your own?"

O'Reilly nodded. "In a British uniform—that's the way
for me to work. I'm going straight from here to Dublin and
enlist as a trooper in the Tenth Hussars—the 'Prince of
Wales' Own,' they like to call themselves. I'll join them with
just one idea in mind—treason against the Crown. It's part
of the Fenian plan to hit the British from within their own
ranks."

His mother spoke. Her voice was quiet, but as he turned
to her he saw that her fingers were white, so tightly was she
gripping her poetry book. "They hang men for treason," she
said simply.

He smiled. "It could be a case of getting hanged, drawn,
and quartered. That's the ugly truth, and I know it. It's a
prospect that's going to make me very careful, and therefore
a much better worker."

His father spoke again. "What can you do in the British
Army? And how do you know they'll have you? The Tenth
Hussars are the pick of the field. They're the best troopers
in the Queen's uniform."

"That's why I chose them." Boyle O'Reilly got to his feet
and began to pace up and down in restless excitement. "I
gave it a lot of thought, Father," he said. "Long before your
letter reached me in Preston, I knew that this was the thing
to do. I knew I'd be coming home to Ireland. Perhaps I
should have come sooner, but I enjoyed my life in England.
And I had a feeling that it would be the last easy pleasure
I'd have for a long time—maybe for the rest of my life. So I
stole a few extra weeks of it before coming back.

"I'd heard about the Fenians' plan of working from the

inside. And I decided then, Father. There's only one goal
worth an Irishman's life, and that's to help make his country
free. Not only free, but independent, too—a nation that can
stand alone and be proud to face the world. That's what you
and Mother always taught me. You were teaching me that
when I was just about able to understand what you were saying. It's what I've learned in my newspaper work. It's what
I've seen in the eyes of Irish exiles. It's what I've read in the
letters from homesick Irishmen who have to live in other
countries.

"I decided that one man on a Dublin newspaper can't do
much to change things from what they are. If our newspapers
had a guaranteed freedom—as they do in the United States—
then we could speak our real thoughts and get the people
behind us like a great army. But in this country the English
can silence any newspaper at any hour of the day or night.
And a silent voice doesn't do anybody any good.

"So I'm going to join the Tenth Hussars. I've talked to
them in Dublin. They'll enlist me whenever I'm ready. I'm
going back to Dublin tomorrow to get into uniform. I chose
that regiment because it's such a proud one. When the treason has spread far enough, and the day comes to strike, the
fact that the Tenth has turned against the Crown will be a
terrible blow to the whole British Army."

His father shrugged, skeptical. "What can one man do in
an army?"

Boyle O'Reilly stopped a moment. He looked down at his
father briefly, and then he went on pacing back and forth
again. "I told you it was a Fenian plot—it's not an O'Reilly
plot. If it's figures you want, there are thousands of us doing
the same thing. Almost one third of the whole British Army
today is Irish, and the Fenians are turning them into revo-

lutionists by the scores each month. No, I'm not a Fenian yet. I haven't joined the group officially. But I will soon. They'll seek me out when they hear what I'm doing. And when they come to me, I'll take their pledge—to throw out the British by force, when and however we can, and let the Irish get the chance to run their own country.

"And we'll have strong help, Father. The Civil War in America will be over someday, and the North will win. It has to win, because of the principle it's fighting for—that men are created equal, and no man should be another's slave regardless of his color.

"There are thousands of Irish-Americans in the ranks of the Northern Army. From some states—Massachusetts, New York, Illinois—they've sent complete regiments under the green flag. Have you heard of them?—the Emmet Guards of Worcester?—the Irish Rifles?—the St. Patrick's Brigade? Every man of them an Irishman!

"They've two scores to settle with England—that England has always oppressed their native land, and that England has put her support behind Jefferson Davis and the Confederate South.

"The Fenians have their agents in the Union Army. When the Civil War ends, they'll have thousands of Irish-American soldiers coming over here in great crowds to help us. I know that's what's developing. I've talked with Fenian members about it, and they've told me of the pledges their agents are getting in America."

His father shook his head. "I wouldn't count on that, John," he said. "It's easy to be enthusiastic and make pledges when there's thousands of miles and a big ocean between that and reality. But when the war in America does end, just remember those Northern soldiers will still be Americans first.

Irish in heart and spirit, of course, but American in their actual lives, with homes to return to and families to care for, and work to be done over there.

"They won't have the money or the ships or the heart to step out of one war and travel all the way over here just to fight in another. They've become Americans now, boy, and that country will be badly hurt before the Civil War is over. They'll be needed at home, and that's where they'll stay."

Boyle O'Reilly disagreed, and said so. "Perhaps someday I'll be back in newspaper work. I'd like to be staying in it now. But the newspapers of Dublin can't do as much good for Ireland today as the men who work inside the British Army—building an army within an army, and getting things ready for the Irish-Americans who are coming over."

The next day he left Dowth Castle and went to Dublin. There he enlisted in the Tenth Hussars, this time not as a part-time Preston volunteer but as a full-time soldier of the Crown. By British standards, then, he was a dark traitor. By Irish standards, he was a courageous patriot. Leaving politics aside, by the standards of any military man he was a good soldier.

He enjoyed the life of a cavalry trooper. He liked martial discipline, the rough male fellowship of the barracks room, the flair and color of the parade ground. He was proud of the uniform of the Tenth Hussars—the dark blue tunic with its heavy braid, the tall plumed busby, the shining boots. He was a good soldier by instinct, and with enough pride in his role to ride his horse now and then past the biggest plate-glass windows in Dublin just so he could get a good look at his own appearance.

He settled easily into the barracks life of Troop D. The commanding officer of the Hussars, Colonel Valentine Baker, recognized his ability as a military man and early offered him promotion. O'Reilly deliberately broke enough rules to have the offer withdrawn, for his point in joining the cavalry was not to win stripes for his own sleeve but to win support in the ranks for an Irish uprising.

There in the barracks with Troop D, then, he began his work. He knew the risk he was taking. He knew that his mission might end with a rope around his neck and with his bloodied severed head being shown on a high pike to warn other Irishmen not to plot against the Crown.

But he knew also that the work would have to be done if Ireland were to be saved as a nation. And he loved Ireland deeply. It was certainly worth his head, he felt, and the heads of thousands of others as well.

By day, though he was proud to go through Dublin in a trooper's uniform, he was even more proud that Dublin was Irish. He saw more beauty in the way the sun reflected on the water of the Liffey River than in the way it glittered on the breastplate of his horse. He saw a brighter color in the green of the trees and the grass than in the gold of a sergeant major's braid. He felt it was pleasant to be smartly clothed and to be part of a brisk troop, but still it was a passing thing. The lasting thing was Ireland.

Awake at night, in the darkness of the barracks room, his mind and his heart would go out to Ireland. In a way, he supposed, he should be bitter that there were any British troops at all abroad in the land. And yet their presence could be the very thing that might lead to breaking the British chain. They were there to be used with plans and action, not just to be resented in sullen silence.

And awake at night, while the rest of the barracks slept, O'Reilly put his plans together. He knew the risk. But he could not see the certainty with which his plans were creating his trap.

4. REBEL IN THE RANKS

JOHN DEVOY was a worried man. He was also a tireless and dedicated Fenian agent. What worried him most at the moment was the fact that no matter how hard he drove himself these days, he seemed unable to satisfy the demands of James Stephens.

Stephens had assigned him the critical position of chief Fenian organizer for the British Army in Ireland. His task took in far more than just spreading unrest and encouraging disloyalty to the Crown. His job also was to oversee the actual creation of the Fenian army within the British Army—to have it manned and officered, ready to strike by day or night at the instant it heard the signal for rebellion.

For a time he had done his job well. Now, late in the summer of 1865, the names on the rebel roster ran into many thousands. But now he had reached a point that seemed to him like the end of the road. He was working as hard as ever, but with no new results. Perhaps, he reasoned, his own fatigue might be the cause, or perhaps the whole revolutionary scheme was losing its spark because of too much planning and too little action. Devoy could not decide where the blame lay. But it was a great worry on his mind, and the cause of unpleasant chiding from Stephens.

He spoke of it now, over a table in Pilsworth's public house on James's Street. It was a safe place to talk, for it was one of the Dublin pubs that catered particularly to the British garrison. On any ordinary night that meant enough singing and shouting and cup-thumping to blanket the words of a private conversation.

His companion in the pub was a civilian agent from Drogheda, a red-haired itinerant veterinary surgeon named
Harry Byrne. On this night they shared two pints of ale at a
corner table, and kept their voices low enough to be ignored
in the clatter and din of a pay-night crowd.

"So, I've done my best," Devoy was complaining, "but my
best is never enough. There'll be no satisfying Stephens, I'm
thinking, till the Queen herself signs the Fenian pledge. I
can build him an army, and he'll still be finding fault."

"He's a sincere man," Byrne observed. "Stephens is sincere."

"So am I," said Devoy. "So are we all. It's not his sincerity
I'm objecting to, and I'm not intending to quit the party.
Don't misunderstand me. At any rate, at this point I couldn't
quit if I wanted to for I'm in the thing up to my chin and
there's no turning back. They've a warrant out for my arrest
right now. They've put soldiers in the roads and lanes about
my home. If I tried to get back to Curragh tonight, just to
sleep in my own bed for once, they'd have my neck in a noose
by sunrise."

Byrne nodded. "A tribute to your work," he said. "It's a
good job you've been doing."

"Perhaps," said Devoy. "But it's tiring. I'm weary. Just in
the past few months I've done enough work against the
Crown to get me a life term in Dartmoor Prison, if ever they
overtake me. That's supposing they didn't want to bother
with a hanging."

They drank their ale in silence for a few moments. They
listened to the bawdy songs of the soldiers, and watched a
fight that broke out in a far corner of the room and that
quickly came to an end.

Byrne picked up the conversation again. "It's hard and
risky work," he agreed. "But Stephens appreciates it. We all

do. We've an army of our own now, thanks to you and your men—an army ready to seize every barracks in the land."

"Not quite." Devoy shook his head. "For the most part, yes —but there's one group that's weak. Worse than that, it's probably the most important of all."

Byrne's eyebrows went up in surprise. "A weak link? You could do with some extra help, then?"

"I could." Devoy nodded. "It's the Tenth Hussars—the 'Prince of Wales' Own.' They're at Island Bridge barracks, out on the western edge of the city. It's an important location —one we'll need to hold when the signal comes. We can't win without it. But I've not found the way to approach any-one there to do our work for us. There are only about a hun-dred Irishmen in the whole regiment. Still, they'd be enough if we could organize them. And what are you smiling at now?"

"The Tenth Hussars? Is that all that's troubling you?"

"Yes." Devoy's face brightened. "You mean you've a way to break it open—a way to get inside?"

Byrne nodded. "You've been studying the wrong men," he said. "I've a good friend in the Tenth—a friend from Dro-gheda. We were boys together. I know how he thinks. He'll do our work for us, and be proud of the chance. In fact, he's probably doing our work for us right now without our know-ing it." Byrne finished his ale in a long swallow, and stood up from the table. "Come along," he said. "We'll go to Island Bridge tonight—right now. I've just the man you want, and we'll find him there. His name is O'Reilly—John Boyle O'Reilly."

Out at the western edge of the city that night, Boyle O'Reilly had been placed on picket duty and assigned to the Royal Barracks. It was a type of army duty he enjoyed, for at some time during the night watch he could expect to be ordered out as a dispatch rider. That always meant the chance to saddle his horse and ride at top speed through the darkness, loving the rush of the wind against his face, loving the beauty of lamplight streaming from windows in the homes he passed, loving the swift beat of his horse's hoofs on the highway, and frankly enjoying the mental picture he had of himself as a dashing courier speeding across the countryside. He could laugh at himself, and still go on enjoying it.

This was just such a night, and the ride would be his. He had been summoned from picket duty and ordered to report to the quarters of Sir Hugh Rose, the commander of the British forces in Ireland. There, he had been handed a dispatch marked for swift delivery to the viceregal lodge. He had hurried to the stables, to get his horse ready for the mission. He had checked his uniform to make certain it was immaculate, from the polished boots and the dark blue trousers to the shining brass chin strap and the cocked-plume busby. He was satisfied with the way he looked.

He was just tightening his saddle girth, and ready to mount and ride, when he raised his head inquiringly at the sound of footsteps on the gravel outside. He frowned as he listened. They didn't sound like normal steps. There was something stealthy and furtive about them, as though the man—no, it sounded like two men—as though the men, then, were abroad on secret business that wouldn't stand too much investigating.

The steps came to a halt just outside the stable. O'Reilly heard an exchange of whispers and then a light tap at the door. His sense of humor rejected the solemn tension of the situation. What was the point of all the secrecy? He straightened up and took a deep breath.

"Come in!" He shouted the invitation.

The door flew open and the two visitors hurried inside and

closed it quickly behind them. One of them, the stocky one, cursed under his breath.

"Damn it, son! You'll be getting us arrested!"

O'Reilly grinned. He did not know the man who'd spoken, but he recognized the other one.

"Harry Byrne," he said, and held out his hand. "I apologize for the loud shouting. I couldn't understand the conspiracy. I thought I'd surprise you."

Byrne smiled back and shook his hand. "You did. And that's just what it is—a conspiracy. You're alone out here?" His glance darted around the stable walls.

Boyle O'Reilly raised his eyebrows. He was interested immediately. "I'm alone, Harry—but I've no time to talk. I'm off with a dispatch from Sir Hugh." He patted the courier pouch on the saddle.

"Just take a moment, then," Byrne said. He still kept his voice low. "We'll arrange to meet later—another time. Shake hands with John Devoy—chief organizer for Stephens."

O'Reilly whistled softly and became serious. "I hear there's a price on your head." He grasped Devoy's hand.

"Not quite," said Devoy, "but there's a fat warrant that keeps me from going home to Curragh. It's the same sort of business that brings me here tonight."

"How did you find me?" O'Reilly asked.

Devoy gestured. "Harry recommended you. I trust his judgment. We rode out from Pilsworth's, and left our horses down the highway. Then we went on foot to Island Bridge and learned you were here. Some of Stephens' men are in the Fifth Dragoon Guards. They slipped us through to the Royal Barracks. They're waiting now to slip us out again. I'll get straight to the point. I want to talk with you about Fenianism—and the men in the Tenth."

O'Reilly nodded. "I'd be glad to listen. Tonight, though, I

haven't the time." As though just remembering, he put his foot in the stirrup and swung into the saddle. "Sir Hugh's business can't wait. I'm sorry, Devoy. Harry, will you swing the door open for me?" The horse began to stamp impatiently.

Devoy put a restraining hand on O'Reilly's boot. "But you're interested?"

"Certainly. But right now I'm under orders."

"Where, then?—and what time?"

"Hoey's pub on Bridgeport Street? Eight o'clock tomorrow night?" O'Reilly waited.

"I'll be there." Devoy stepped back.

"Just one thing puzzles me."

"What's that?"

O'Reilly looked down at him and chuckled. "I'd heard about you. I'd been wondering when you'd hear about me. What kept you away so long?"

Byrne pushed open the door. O'Reilly slapped his horse on the flank and galloped off into the night. He felt good about the strange meeting. He'd be at Hoey's on time, and pledge himself to the conspiracy.

It was a profitable partnership for the Fenian movement. From the time of their first meeting in the stable, Boyle O'Reilly and John Devoy made contact almost every day—at Pilsworth's on James's Street, at Hoey's on Bridgeport Street, at Fortune's, at Barclay's, at the Two Soldiers—at one or another of the Dublin pubs where the Fenian agents met over beer glasses and mingled with the British troops.

Already Boyle O'Reilly had spread some of the seeds of rebellion in the ranks of the Tenth Hussars. He had done it in a subtle way, without breaking the rules of the normal life of the barracks. He had talked at times sadly and dejectedly

about Ireland's hunger, about thin crops, about famine
creeping through the farmlands; and he had sometimes
swung the talk abruptly to British landowners, and to their
larders well stocked with British beef. He had taken over the
leadership in song fests and amateur theatricals, and had
found it easy to inject a line of satire and derision here and
there against the British. He had gone about his work softly
whistling old Irish tunes, and had heard them catch on with
others. And occasionally he had left a rebel symbol where it
could be seen, scratched on a table top or outlined in the
sand by the barracks door.

He had done nothing openly violent enough or dramatic
enough to cause his arrest, and probably none of his officers
suspected what he was doing. But unrest was spreading, and
forming a deepening pool of resentment against the British.

Meanwhile, the government had sensed what was going on
without knowing its source. Boyle O'Reilly knew there were
many besides himself who were doing the same quiet work,
and that for the time, at least, there was little chance of his
being caught. Now he was able to improve his work, though,
through his partnership with Devoy—through inviting his
barracks mates to stop in for a drink at Barclay's or Fortune's
or wherever Stephens' agents would be at the moment. And
there, too, the subtle spreading of unrest would be fed and
nursed and studied.

In this way, in a matter of less than four months, Boyle
O'Reilly put into Devoy's hands eighty men who took the
Fenian oath and swore to fight to the death for Ireland—to
fight, that their children might go to school, their families
to Mass, their neighbors to an open political meeting without
fear of being arrested and beaten. And with those eighty men
the Fenians gained gate keys, military papers, and strategic

British defense plans carefully detailed on maps. The plot was working well.

Finally everything seemed ready. The day came when all that was needed was the signal. Then Boyle O'Reilly in the Tenth Hussars and other Fenians in the other regiments would give the loud cry that would lead their organized mutineers into open battle against the British force that contained them. The planning was complete, but the signal never came. England had not been asleep.

Some weeks earlier British police had made a swift and secret raid on the offices of Stephens' newspaper, *The Irish People*. They had arrested its editors—O'Donovan Rossa, Thomas Luby, John O'Leary, and Stephens himself. And in staging the raid, the British had seized all the files and correspondence in Stephens' headquarters. Suddenly they had in their hands the complete plans for the uprising of some 15,000 troops who were numbered in the Fenian ranks. In one move they had found the weapon that would smash the whole rebellion.

There was no swift wave of arrests, no sudden violence or seizure of the rebels. There was no need for any such action, for the Fenian troops themselves knew nothing of the prize the British had captured. Only the editors knew, and they were behind bars, safely cut off from outside communication.

That winter the British acted carefully and deliberately before moving to break the planned uprising. Not until February 12, 1866, when they had laid their plans with accuracy and had just the right men in the right places—not until then did they show their hand.

Boyle O'Reilly saw them from a distance that day, and he knew at once what was happening. He was standing at a barracks window at Island Bridge looking out idly and watching a group of his mates approach along the walkway. And as he watched, suddenly he tensed and felt his spine go cold. He was witness to something almost incredible. How could anyone have known!

He saw a squad of military police move out and halt the walking group—saw them seize two men he knew to be Fenians, and let the rest pass on. At the far side of the parade ground he saw the same thing happening again—three men being seized—men he knew to be Fenians. And the rest being left untouched. Suddenly and quietly it was taking place all through the garrison area. The rebels were being singled out and herded into the guardhouse. With scarcely a sound all the bright plans for revolution were vanishing like stars before a rising storm.

Boyle O'Reilly watched in growing bitterness for a few more minutes, and then he turned helplessly from the window. There was nothing to be done, nothing anybody could do now. He sat dejectedly on the edge of his bed, and thought of the years of work and hope slipping away—of the rebuilding that would have to go on in Ireland—even in countries abroad. Then he thought of himself, and nodded his head.

"My turn will come next," he said in a slow voice.

His barracks mates looked across at him, puzzled. They had no idea what was on his mind. But they did not have long to wait before finding out. A heavy fist came pounding at the barracks door. The door was flung open, and O'Reilly saw two military policemen standing there, waiting. Without a word he stood up and walked to meet them. There was no good now in arguing or pretending. No sense to anything but surrender.

The two troopers swung about as he stepped between them. The sound of their footsteps was hollow along the corridor. He heard the closing of the door behind, cutting him off forever from a soldier's life in Ireland.

5. ARBOR HILL

THE HEAVY IRON GATES of Arbor Hill military prison clanged shut in his face. And they left him alone with his thoughts for many days.

Suddenly, where there had been the congenial and mildly exciting life of a soldier in garrison, now there was only the lonesome and bleak routine of a prisoner in his cell. Where there had been the green grass of Ireland to see, and the busy streets to stroll, now there were only bare walls and the weak gray daylight that sometimes found its way in from the world outside. He saw no other men now, except the warder who brought him his food, and the guard who kept him under close watch for a brief daily exercise period in the prison yard.

For many days, then, they left Boyle O'Reilly with his thoughts. And they did it deliberately, to soften him for his coming trial, hoping to see him break before that time. They gave him hours and days and weeks to think of his childhood and his home and his friends and his faults.

But Boyle O'Reilly was a man of strength, and the ordeal failed to work. His thoughts were not of remorse for what he had done, but of regret that he had failed and had been thrown into prison where he could fight no more. Perhaps, though—perhaps at that, he still might have accomplished something—might have struck one small blow for Ireland. He wondered about that. He wondered, because he remembered a small incident that had happened on the day of his arrest. They'd been taking him through the barracks yard, bound for Arbor Hill, when the commanding officer of the

Tenth had come striding across the grass, deliberately inter-
cepting the guards on their path. Colonel Baker had always
liked O'Reilly, and had pointedly set up for him one opportunity after another in the hope of seeing him make the army
his career.

Now, in this instance, he had confronted O'Reilly in a
blaze of anger and had shaken his big fist in the prisoner's
face. He had cried out, in a voice that could be heard even
in the distant barracks rooms:

"Damn you, O'Reilly! Damn you! You've ruined the best
regiment in the service!"

Then the colonel had swung about abruptly and marched
off to his quarters, and O'Reilly had noticed that Baker's
head seemed to bow lower with each step until at last he was
out of sight.

Alone in his Arbor Hill cell, O'Reilly wondered about
that. Had he ruined the best regiment in the service? If so,
he had done something for Ireland, for no matter how much
he'd loved his life with the Tenth Hussars, any British regiment on Irish garrison duty was still just a weapon of control
for British rule. Perhaps he had blunted one weapon. It
pleased him to think that he had.

Then, too, he had helped plant the seeds of dissension, and
there was no telling what the crop would be. The mass arrests of Fenians in the ranks would be talked about in barracks rooms for years to come, and the story would spread
from one army post to another wherever the empire sent its
troops. With all its power, England could never stop that
from happening nor stop the story from growing. Perhaps,
then, there had been some success, even though the uprising
itself had been crushed without a shot.

There was little to do in the cell at Arbor Hill except to
think such thoughts and wait for day to follow day, and week

to follow week, in a meaningless file. He had expected that, in time, when they thought he had weakened under silence and loneliness, the prison officials would try to break him down and drain him of information. And so they did. He had guessed right; they tried to make him an informer.

They came to him in his cell, seeming grim one day and sympathetic the next, smiling one time and threatening another. They hurled hundreds of questions at him, hammering away at tiny points, probing into all angles of the Fenian plan. They grilled him in relays, and for hours at a time, patiently waiting for him to break, or even to bend.

They promised him immunity if he would tell all he knew, and they threatened him with terrible torture if he did not. They lied to him about what the other prisoners were saying, and they tried to convince him that he alone was holding out and being stubborn—that the others had talked freely and were being repaid with an easy and comfortable life. And Boyle O'Reilly knew they lied.

"Come, now," they said to him. "Be sensible, man—make it easy for yourself. You've nothing to lose by talking. Tell us where Stephens is hiding."

O'Reilly smiled to himself at that blunder. So Stephens had escaped, had he?

"Where's John Devoy?" they demanded. "You know their hideouts. You know their schemes. Do you suppose they'd suffer if they were in your place? Not them! They'd talk their heads off and make the most of it. You'd better do the same."

O'Reilly kept silent. So Stephens had escaped, and apparently they'd never had their hands on Devoy. With those two still at large, Fenianism was a long way from dead.

"Come now, O'Reilly," the prodding went on. "Your friends have been smart. They've been helpful. They've told us what they know, and we've been easy with them. They're

walking around outside right now. You could join them tonight, if you'd answer our questions. That would be good,
wouldn't it?—to have ale and beef with them at Pilsworth's
instead of living alone here like a criminal? Come now, all
you have to do is to talk.

"Tell us, O'Reilly. What about Sergeant McCarthy and
Corporal Chambers? When did they join the Fenians? Did
you ever see them with Devoy?—or with Stephens?—or John
Breslin? Would Breslin and Stephens be hiding out together?"

So Breslin was still at large, too. That was good news. He
was one of the best of the civilian organizers; a great patriot
and an intelligent agent.

"You'd better start talking, O'Reilly," they went on. "Mc-
Carthy and Chambers were your close friends, but don't
think they haven't told us what we wanted to know about
you. They were sensible, son. They talked and were helpful,
and now they'll be out with their pretty girls tonight, while
you'll be sitting here alone. Wouldn't you like to be meeting
an easy wench tonight? We can arrange it, O'Reilly. Be
smart, like your friends."

He smiled to himself when they talked like that, for the
longer he held out and stayed silent the more his wardens
were helping him. They were telling him the very things he
wanted to know, while trying to learn the things he would
not tell.

Devoy and Stephens and Breslin still at large. Very good.
And obviously McCarthy and Chambers were getting the
same treatment he was getting. He had wondered about that,
too—wondered what had happened to his closest friends.
Now he knew they were here in Arbor Hill, somewhere close
by. So they'd be out with pretty girls tonight?—certainly not
Charles McCarthy, with his big loyal heart and his great love

for his wife and three children—and certainly not Tom Chambers, who could talk endlessly about his girl from Cork and their plans to marry this coming summer.

No, not one of them would be out for a long time to come. Jim Wilson, Tom Hassett, Jim Darragh, Martin Hogan—all the others. They'd stay behind prison bars probably for the rest of their lives, he reflected—either that or be put to death. And not one of them would turn informer. He was convinced that they were all getting the same treatment—the wheedling, threatening, coaxing—and that not one of the band ever would sell out to the British.

And so it went, week after week and month after month. Boyle O'Reilly marked the days on the walls of his cell, while the British Crown moved slowly to prepare the Fenians' trials.

Outside, the cold gray Irish winter turned to spring. The chill rains stopped. The sun shone warmer each day, and the grass and flowers and birds began to respond with new life. At night, moving in from the sea, the soft mist brought with it a smell of salt that sometimes found its way into the cells and corridors of Arbor Hill. O'Reilly breathed it in, lying awake on his blanket in the darkness, and thinking how pleasant it would be to enjoy the sounds and colors and scents of the outside world once more. He wondered how many years might pass, and in what land he might find himself, if that freedom ever came to him again. He wondered whether it would be better to be given a death sentence and lose everything at once, or to live behind stone walls and iron bars and never be able to know what was happening beyond.

His cell was his only world. He tried to write poems, sometimes scratching them on the walls and on the floor. He tried to talk to other prisoners by tapping on the water pipes; and although answering taps came back, there could be no conversation for they had not arranged a code. The sun climbed higher with the seasons, and brought more light to his room. Then, at last, the guards came to lead him away for trial. Boyle O'Reilly welcomed their coming, for this at least would end the uncertainty and the waste of time.

They held his trial in the messroom of the Eighty-fifth Regiment at Royal Barracks. It opened on June 27, 1866, on the day before his twenty-second birthday. They brought him in and sat him roughly in the prisoner's dock, and he looked around at some of the small things he recognized from visits here in other times—a picture, a flaw in the window glass, a small stain on the wall near the far corner.

Sitting alongside, he recognized some of his barracks mates under guard. McCarthy was there. And Privates Pat Keating and Mike Harrington and James Darragh. He wondered why Chambers was missing.

The court guard standing close to him seemed to be a sympathetic man. O'Reilly decided to risk a rebuke by speaking to him; there was nothing at all to lose. He watched steadily, until he caught the guard's eye, then whispered to him softly.

"Where's Tom Chambers?"

The guard hesitated an instant, as though to cling to discipline. Then, with a barely noticeable shrug, he returned the whisper.

"They tried him last month. Guilty and waitin' sentence."

One or two court officers glanced their way, annoyed by the whispering but unsure of its source. O'Reilly stayed quiet rather than get the guard in trouble. He waited patiently for the court to open its session. Looking around, he recognized Colonel Sawyer of the Sixth Dragoon Guards as president of the court-martial board, looking uncompromising with his

sharp gray mustache and florid face and eyes like twin dag-
gers. The prosecutor was a Captain Whelan of the Eighth
Regiment, stout and bald and afraid of the colonel. O'Reilly
did not recognize either the judge advocate or the defense
attorneys. And of the fourteen other officers of the court, only
one was from the Tenth Hussars. He decided to act as his
own attorney, if the court would allow it.

A loud voice broke in on his thoughts. The men were
rising to their feet. Court-martial was in session. O'Reilly
hastily got up from his chair in the dock.

The voice cried out the charge:

". . . having at Dublin, in January 1866, come to the
knowledge of an intended mutiny in Her Majesty's Forces in
Ireland, and not giving information of said intended mutiny
to his commanding officer . . ."

O'Reilly caught Charles McCarthy looking at him with an
amused light in his eyes, and he returned the look the same
way. He knew that each was thinking the same thing: this
wasn't as bad as they'd expected, for the government obviously lacked the evidence to make it that bad. The charge
was lighter than they'd dared to hope for. It could still mean
a death sentence, but it was far from a direct charge of mutiny. "Having knowledge" and "failing to give information"
—easier to find guilt there, but far different from open mutiny—and far harder to justify a hanging.

The Government, then, had not been able to find the informers it needed. Apparently nobody had talked except a
few paid British spies who had penetrated the Fenian ranks.

McCarthy suddenly looked relaxed and confident. O'Reilly
winked across at him quickly, in the confusion of sitting
down.

Then, abruptly, he was prodded to his feet again, to answer
the call of his name:

". . . the case of Private John Boyle O'Reilly, Tenth Hussars. How pleads the prisoner, guilty or not guilty?"

"Not guilty!" O'Reilly cried.

His voice caught the defense attorney halfway standing, and the man turned around with a surprised look in his eyes. "You wish to handle your own case, O'Reilly?"

"I do—with the permission of the court."

Colonel Sawyer stared down at him grimly from his seat at the head of the board. "Permission granted," he said. "It's your privilege—and I remind you that it's your risk as well."

O'Reilly nodded briefly. "I accept the risk."

"Be seated." Sawyer gestured at him. "Captain Whelan, you will open the case for the Government."

Boyle O'Reilly tried to hold his attention on Whelan's words. It was important to listen. Life or death could hang on any word in a trial of this sort. He exchanged quick glances with McCarthy again, and then bowed his head to stare at the floor and concentrate on what the prosecutor was saying.

"The enormity of the offense with which the prisoner is charged," Whelan exclaimed, striding up and down before the board, "is such that it is difficult to find language to describe it!

"It strikes at the root of all military discipline. If allowed to escape the punishment which it entails, it would render Her Majesty's forces—who ought to be the guardians of our lives and liberty, and the bulwark and protection of the constitution under which we live—it would render them, I say, a source of danger to the state and all its loyal citizens and subjects.

"Her Majesty's faithful subjects would become the prey and victims of military despotism, licentiousness, and violence! Our standing army would then be a terror to the throne! It would be a curse—not a blessing—to the community.

"It will be for you, gentlemen, to say whether the evidence which shall be placed before you leaves upon your mind any reasonable doubt of the prisoner's guilt.

"Gentlemen, I shall now present the evidence to show that prisoner O'Reilly was an active member of the Fenian conspiracy, and that he tried to induce other soldiers to join it.

"For the Government's first witness——" Whelan turned to the prosecutor's table, and consulted his notes. He straightened up, and turned back to the court. "Lance Corporal Fitzgerald of the Tenth Hussars, please take the witness stand."

It was a battle for his life now, and Boyle O'Reilly straightened up to meet it, ready to pounce upon the first flaw that showed up in any man's testimony.

6. "TO BE HANGED . . ."

THE TRIAL had barely begun. Only a few words had been spoken. But already Boyle O'Reilly saw with cold clarity the danger that he faced.

It came to him like a stunning blow that he was to have no chance whatever. He was to be convicted, no matter what was said, no matter what took place. The Government had made its decision before opening the trial. Rules of testimony and evidence were to be ignored from the start. Procedure was to be a thing of convenience for the Crown, to be twisted and violated at will.

He realized immediately what was happening, and he stared unbelievingly at the members of the board, waiting for one of them to rise in protest and demand a fair trial. Instead, they sat comfortably in their uniforms, ignoring the violations of court rules, gazing out of the windows, examining their fingernails, toying with pencil and paper. Their expressions, when they looked at O'Reilly, amounted to studied hostility.

He glanced across briefly at McCarthy, seated among the other prisoners. They exchanged helpless shrugs. There was nothing to be done—no place to reach with an appeal. He turned back again, to pay attention to the witness. Why bother with a trial at all? he wondered.

He remembered this Corporal Fitzgerald well. They'd had drinks together many a time, in many a pub, and they'd been good barracks companions. He remembered introducing Fitzgerald to Devoy. And he remembered hoping that Devoy had made a Fenian of him, but he'd never been certain. Now it was all coming out, from Fitzgerald himself. Devoy had tried, and had failed.

"I was with O'Reilly in Hoey's public house on Bridgeport Street," the corporal was testifying. "That was in November 1865. O'Reilly took me there and introduced me to a man named Devoy."

Captain Whelan broke in for the prosecution. "Was there any conversation in the presence of the prisoner? If so, tell us what it was."

O'Reilly jumped to his feet instantly. "I object, sir!" he cried. "This relates to a conversation that took place previous to the date of the charge. The charge specifies January, and the witness is talking about November."

Colonel Sawyer glared at him angrily. "Sit down, prisoner! The evidence is admissible. Objection overruled." He nodded impatiently at Fitzgerald, who suddenly seemed frightened and unsure of himself. "Go on with your story, Corporal."

O'Reilly sat back in dismay. He'd have little chance of being heard on anything, that was apparent. There was little to do, then, but to listen to the story unfold, and hold back his objections until something more critical came along.

"I met O'Reilly in town one evening," Fitzgerald went on, "and we spoke of some arrests that had been made that day, and I said, 'This business is getting serious.'"

Colonel Sawyer broke in. "What did you mean by the words 'this business,' Corporal?"

"I meant the Fenian conspiracy, sir," Fitzgerald replied.

The colonel looked pleased. "Continue."

"O'Reilly asked me to meet him later at the Sign of the Two Soldiers," Fitzgerald said. "I went there and waited for him. He came in and ordered drinks and then asked me to go with him to Hoey's, where he wanted to introduce me to somebody. We went to Hoey's—to the upstairs room—and he introduced me to John Devoy.

"Devoy told me O'Reilly had spoken to him several times about me, and that they wanted to get me to join them. We three were sitting at a table then, drinking beer.

"I asked Devoy who was behind the Fenian affair, and he told me Stephens was. I asked him about arms and ammunition. Devoy said there was plenty, and that a lot more was arriving every day from America. I asked who were to be the officers, and Devoy said it was being planned so that the privates would not know their noncommissioned officers beforehand, nor they their superior officers.

"Then Devoy and O'Reilly left the room together, and I waited for them. O'Reilly came back alone and said that Devoy wanted to see me outside. I went down to the yard and found Devoy there. There were just the two of us. He said, 'I suppose O'Reilly has told you what I want with you.'"

O'Reilly jumped to his feet again and faced Colonel Sawyer. "I object, sir!" he said. "What the witness now states to have taken place was not in my presence. It is not admissible."

"Overruled," said the colonel. "Sit down."

O'Reilly returned to his seat, to hear still more of the story building up against him and to ponder the uselessness of trying to fight it on points of legality.

It was all true—what Fitzgerald had said, and what he was saying now. It was true that he had brought Fitzgerald and Devoy together, hoping to recruit the corporal for the Fenians. And it was true, he supposed, that Fitzgerald had refused to take the oath before returning from the pub yard with Devoy. They'd had another round of beer, then, and the meeting at Hoey's had ended. The Fenians had wanted Fitz-

gerald in their ranks badly. His twelve years of soldiering
would have been highly valuable in training young recruits.
But they had tried and failed, and they never had approached
him again.

It was all true, O'Reilly knew; but every step had been
carefully planned with the knowledge that someday there
might be arrests and trials—and each critical point had been
handled in such a way as to make it inadmissible in court-
room testimony. That was the way the Fenians tried to handle as much of their affairs as possible; it was wise to have
caution as well as vision. It was all wasted, though, with a
man such as Colonel Sawyer running the trial. Rules obviously meant nothing to him when they stood in the way of a
conviction.

O'Reilly glanced over at the messroom window, and at the
sunshine flooding in from the outside. If this was the way
the trial was to be run, he reflected—and if he escaped a
hanging—it would be many years before he'd walk freely in
the sunshine again, or know the soft colors of the Irish countryside, or see the trout swirling in the Boyne River.

But Fitzgerald was stepping down now, and another witness was walking to the stand. It was another barracks mate,
Private McDonald of the Tenth Hussars, a tall, dark-haired
horseman who could ride all day and drink all night and still
report clear-eyed for picket duty in the morning. O'Reilly
knew him well. McDonald gave him a sidelong glance of encouragement as he strode toward the witness stand. O'Reilly
wondered what it meant. He found out in the next few
minutes.

From the start McDonald's testimony irritated the court-
martial board. It was clear and orderly, but it was subtly
lined with a mood of sympathy for the defendant and a touch
of contempt for the methods being used against him. It

brought O'Reilly to the edge of his chair with the first real feeling of hope he'd had since entering the room.

"Yes, I was at Pilsworth's with the prisoner about Christmas-time," McDonald was saying. "We went there together, as we often did. There were other persons there, but I can't say who they were. There were civilians there, too, but I did not know their names."

Whelan broke in. "Was John Devoy there?"

"I've learned since then that Devoy was present," McDonald replied. "O'Reilly did not introduce me to any civilians on that occasion. Any drinks that we had, we paid for them ourselves. And there was no conversation about Fenianism in the presence of the prisoner."

Colonel Sawyer jerked upright. His mustache bristled. He slammed his fist on the table and glared angrily at McDonald.

"Remember you're under oath!" he warned.

McDonald acknowledged the warning with a respectful nod, and went on with his testimony.

"The prisoner was sitting near me for a quarter of an hour or more," he said. "He was sitting alongside me, as close as one person usually sits to another. I had some conversation with O'Reilly while he was sitting there with me. I can't say now what it was about. But it was not about Fenianism."

The colonel scowled and lurched forward again. Then he checked himself and sat back. O'Reilly exchanged a look of satisfaction with McCarthy; two points in favor of the defense, in case anybody in court was keeping score.

"Tell us about John Devoy," Whelan directed the witness.

"I was not personally acquainted with John Devoy," McDonald said. "I know him by sight now, but I did not know him then. O'Reilly and I were sitting at a big table, and others were sitting there, too. Several of them were strangers to me. I know now that John Devoy was sitting there that night, but I did not speak to him nor he to me.

"Another time O'Reilly and I went together to Fortune's pub in Golden Lane. I forget just when it was, but it was after Christmas, I think. There were other soldiers there that night—infantrymen. I don't remember who they were, or even if I knew them. And there were civilians, too. Devoy was one of the civilians. There were——"

"Just a moment, witness," Colonel Sawyer interrupted sharply, and McDonald faced him in silence.

"Is it possible you don't know the name of a single infantryman who was present? We want facts at this trial."

McDonald nodded. "I do not know their names," he said.

"What regiments did they belong to?"

"Some from the Sixty-first, some from the Eighty-seventh. O'Reilly and I were the only cavalrymen present."

"Go on with your story," Colonel Sawyer ordered.

McDonald hesitated a moment, as though to collect his thoughts. Then he continued.

"Civilians that we don't know," he said, "frequently offer to buy drinks for us in public houses. It happens to all soldiers.

"At Fortune's place, Devoy bought drinks for me and O'Reilly. He asked us to join a group that was going on to Doyle's pub, and we went there with several infantrymen and three civilians. Devoy was one of them. More civilians bought us drinks there at Doyle's. I heard no conversation between O'Reilly and the others about Fenianism."

He paused, to let the statement take effect.

"Proceed!" Colonel Sawyer's voice was terse.

"A fortnight later," McDonald said, "I went with O'Reilly to Barclay's pub, and again there were both civilians and sol-

diers present. Devoy was there that night. A week later we
went again to Hoey's, but O'Reilly did not stay. He went
away soon after we were inside. Another time we went to
Bergin's place on James's Street, and I did not know any of
the persons present. There was singing for a while. There
was no conversation between O'Reilly and the others."

"No conversation?" Sawyer demanded.

"None, sir."

The colonel curled his lip. "The pubs are getting to be
mortal slow places, according to your account. Is that all you
have to say?"

"Yes, sir."

"Prisoner"—nodding at O'Reilly—"you may cross-exam-
ine the witness."

O'Reilly got to his feet. He saw a trace of a satisfied smile
flick across McDonald's lips. He decided not to tamper with
the good work McDonald had done, but merely to emphasize
a point or two. McDonald would know what he had in mind.

"At any of the places you've mentioned," O'Reilly said,
"did we ever discuss Fenianism?"

McDonald's answer was concise. "We had no conversation
about Fenianism at Fortune's. We had none at Hoey's. We
had none at Barclay's or Doyle's or Bergin's or Pilsworth's.
I think that covers them all."

"Thank you," said O'Reilly, and sat down.

But Sawyer was not through yet. "Just a moment," he said.
He pinned McDonald with a stare. "You testified there was
singing at the pubs. Answer this direct question: Were the
songs Fenian songs?"

"No, sir! They were not."

O'Reilly jumped to his feet. "Weren't they chiefly Irish
love songs?"

"I don't know," said McDonald, flustered.

"Did I ever tell you Devoy was a friend of mine or of my family?"

"No, you did not."

"Did I ever talk to you about Fenianism? Any place or any time?"

"Never." McDonald swung his eyes to Colonel Sawyer. "John O'Reilly never spoke to me about Fenianism and I never heard any Fenian songs in his company!"

"How do you know what's a Fenian song and what isn't?" Sawyer demanded.

"I don't know. Irish songs, I guess."

Sawyer waved him away with a gesture of scorn.

The trial dragged on for twelve days. On the record O'Reilly was convinced he could win a dismissal; on the mood of the court-martial board he knew he would lose.

It didn't matter that he was never allowed to present his case without interference and official heckling. It didn't matter that two government witnesses—Privates Dennis Denny and John Smith of the Tenth Hussars—gave contradictory testimony amounting to perjury on the part of one or the other. Nor did it matter that the witnesses for the prosecution were unable to present any solid, incriminating evidence against O'Reilly. None of that mattered, for the verdict clearly had been agreed upon before the trial opened.

Even two paid informers who testified for the prosecution failed to link O'Reilly with actual Fenian activity. One of these was a notorious professional informer named Talbot. He failed even to mention O'Reilly in his story, but merely furnished evidence that a conspiracy did exist—that it probably had touched every regiment in Ireland.

The other was Private Patrick Foley of the Tenth Hussars. He did not implicate O'Reilly.

"Yes, I took the oath," Foley said. "But I did not call God

to witness I would keep it. I had a Testament in my hand and I went through the motions of kissing it, but I didn't really do so. When I took the Fenian oath, most decidedly I intended to become an informer."

Then, abruptly, the trial was ended.

Captain Whelan's summary was brief. He spent a minimum of time reviewing the case, and then he said:

"The court should bear in mind that it has the burden of proving its charges. It is not up to the prisoner to disprove them.

"Now, on a calm and fair review of the evidence—granting the prisoner everything that contains a reasonable doubt—straining nothing against him—now, is the court satisfied that the facts are inconsistent with any other conclusion than the prisoner's guilt? Is the court satisfied that the Fenians intended mutiny? Is the court satisfied that the prisoner knew of that intention?"

In his own heart, Boyle O'Reilly knew what the answer to that would be—the court was so satisfied, and had been since the first moment of the trial. The whole performance had been rigged, probably as a warning to other soldiers never to get involved with a movement of rebellion. O'Reilly was to be an example, and so were Chambers and McCarthy, Darragh and Hassett, Wilson and Hogan, and all the rest of them.

To himself, he admitted his own guilt. He had gambled and lost, and in a way deserved exactly what he was getting. But, he told himself, the approach to punishment was a cruel one and unfair in every respect. The Government had lost the case on evidence and won it on might. It was an example of the very type of tyranny and despotism he had pledged himself to fight against when he had willingly taken the Fenian oath.

On July 9, then, he sat in the prisoner's dock to hear his sentence, and he knew beforehand what it would be. Colonel Sawyer glared at him with sardonic animosity, and waved him to his feet to hear the judgment. It was exactly what he'd expected:

". . . to be hanged by the neck until dead!"

II

CHAINS

(1866–1869)

Even so, they are better than those who bend
Like beasts to the lash, and go on to the end
As a beast will go, with today for a life,
And tomorrow a blank. Offer peace and strife
To a man enslaved—let him vote for ease
And coward labor, and be content;
Or let him go out in the front, as these,
With their eyes on the doom and the danger, went.

        From "The Mutiny of the Chains."

7. IRON JUSTICE

IT WAS THE AFTERNOON of September 3, a rare golden afternoon even for Ireland. Boyle O'Reilly tried to drink in its beauty, wanting to pull it within him through his eyes and his flesh, for he knew that he might never again stand in such sunshine and feel the soil of Ireland beneath his feet.

He stood with McCarthy and Chambers in the center of the parade ground before the Royal Barracks. The three were in full uniform for the last time in their lives. They might have been brothers—each standing straight and dark and proud—brothers, perhaps, who had been singled out for military honors and were waiting at attention for the moment to receive them. They shared instead the brotherhood of a conspiracy against a ruling power, and a devotion to their country, and there could be pride in that, too.

The sound of beating drums and marching feet came to O'Reilly's ears, growing louder. He watched the last of the attending troop companies march across Royal Square and wheel into formation at the edge of the parade ground. He wondered briefly how McCarthy and Chambers felt, waiting to hear their sentence read in public, waiting resignedly to be stripped of their uniforms. McCarthy, he supposed, would be thinking of his wife and children, and probably torturing himself with worry, wondering how they'd be taken care of now, and longing to see their faces for a last lingering moment. Tom Chambers would be thinking of the girl in Cork, the sweetheart who would never bear his children now— never share his bread, nor walk with him down green pathways, nor grow old with him in the simple comfort of their own home.

He wondered if many of the other men on the parade ground—the soldiers who had been ordered to witness this moment—were concealing thoughts like his. He met the eyes of some in the ranks that were close at hand. And he saw in their faces no look of scorn or condemnation, no awareness of disgrace. He saw sympathy there instead, and comradeship and respect. It encouraged him, for it made him feel that there always would be others to fight the same oppression he had fought—that as fast as some men were trapped and removed, others would step forward to carry on the struggle for tolerance and freedom, until at last someday it would succeed.

Abruptly at that moment his thoughts were broken by a roll of drums and the bright notes of a bugle, sounding Attention. A group of officers, four abreast, came marching smartly across the parade ground. One of them carried a rolled paper in his right hand. That, O'Reilly knew, would be the official document of sentence, to be read in the open for all to hear.

Somehow in the days that had passed since the trial word had reached him that the death sentence for all three had been commuted—that it was to be life imprisonment instead. But that didn't matter much now. There was no cause for rejoicing in a sentence that would condemn him to years of being punished and driven and caged like a beast. It might be better, after all, to have it come to an end at once.

He heard the start of the reading, but he gave it little attention. He tried, instead, to take in all the beauty of the bright afternoon, realizing that he'd never know another quite like it. He let his eyes travel over the soft green of the Irish turf, the pools of golden sunshine beneath a distant tree, the brick-red color of the barracks wall outlined against a blue sky. He listened closely to the songs of the birds and felt glad for them because they were happy and free. He drew deep breaths of the fresh, clear air, and felt the touch of the light breeze against his cheeks. All this he would carry with him in memory to whatever dark days lay ahead; and no man could take it from him.

There was a rustle and a movement in the ranks, and he pulled himself back to the moment at hand. Yes, that was it—the reading was ended. It was to be life imprisonment, after all, and not a quick hanging. Life imprisonment with severe physical punishment and hard labor, and with six months of solitary confinement at the start.

Fresh orders were shouted. The three prisoners heard them and obeyed. They were stripped of their uniforms. There on the parade ground they were handed the shapeless garb of the convict's dress. And in another moment, where three soldiers had stood in full regalia, now there stood three felons looking grotesquely out of place in the midst of military finery.

O'Reilly glanced for the last time at his cavalry dress, now held in the hands of a stranger. He looked at the dark blue cloth and the heavy braid as he might have looked at a close friend in saying farewell. He had loved the uniform and the life of a cavalry rider; but more than that, he had loved the dream of an Ireland where all the uniforms would be Irish. One or the other had had to go, and he had made the choice that held honor.

And now it was time for the chains and the journey into suffering and misery and punishment.

It was bitterly cold that winter, and the ice-like fingers of the freeze stretched in through granite prison walls and clutched at the men inside—the men who could not escape its reach. It was with them always, the cold and the solitude, the silence and the despair. It was with them all day and all night.

The three of them had been brought to England in chains. They had been marched together through the streets of Dublin, shackled like animals, their heavy iron links jangling as they walked. There had been no other sound all along the way to the ship except the clanking of their chains and the shuffling of their feet. Except for that, a weird silence had moved with them, enveloping them, preceding them, following them, penetrating to the little groups that watched them pass by and looked at them with wordless sympathy or open scorn. But all of that had been in the warmth of September, before the unexplained shifting of the three men from one English prison to another.

Pentonville Prison, with its roofless cells and the privilege of pacing back and forth between narrow walls for one hour each day.

Chatham, where the prisoners worked in the brickyards, chained together, and where they were paraded through the town streets almost daily, to be hooted at and ridiculed by the onlookers. Chatham, with thirty days on bread and water for an escape attempt that failed.

Portsmouth, with no rest from morning till night, carrying the bricks that were made by a relentless machine that never slowed. Portsmouth and another thirty days on bread and water, for another escape attempt that failed.

But Millbank Prison in London was the worst. Millbank, with its dark and clammy corners and its maddening solitude —for Millbank meant the six months of heatless solitary confinement that stretched through the long and bitter winter.

They placed him in a cold stone cell, behind an iron-barred door that bore a small card. The card read: JOHN

BOYLE O'REILLY, 20 YEARS. He read the inscription without any feeling of emotion. Sudden death, or life imprisonment, or twenty years of misery—it didn't matter which was his lot. And it didn't matter that somebody in high office had reduced the sentence, possibly because of the way the trial had been handled. It didn't matter, he reflected, because in the end the result would be the same—a life removed from society, wrecked and tossed aside. It was the price he'd have to pay for fighting against an intolerant power that was stronger than those who rejected it. And the only way to avoid the payment was to keep a patient vigil for a chance to escape.

In Millbank there was no such chance. Boyle O'Reilly resigned himself to that almost as soon as he stepped past the iron-barred door and entered his cell. The dungeon they had put him in had bare stone walls and a cold stone floor. It was eight feet wide and nine feet long—just long enough for him to take three paces in one direction, turn, and take three paces back. He tried that, when first they slammed the door behind him—three steps forward, three steps back. An angry shout from a guard in the corridor brought him to a quick halt.

"You, there! O'Reilly! No walking in the cells!"

O'Reilly stared at the guard through the iron bars in stunned disbelief. No walking in the cells? That was incredible.

"One hour a day you walk in the yard, O'Reilly." The guard grinned at him with malice. "And one hour a day you scrub your cell—soon as you're off the bed in the morning. For the rest, you sit—or stand and don't move. That's the rules, and I'm here to make you obey."

O'Reilly felt a surge of despair. Six months of idle sitting or motionless standing in the gray half-light of a cold cell— he who had ridden with cavalrymen, boxed with local cham-

pions, raced across fields for the joy of running, plunged into
streams for the joy of swimming. *"No walking in the cells,
O'Reilly!"* Yes, the hanging might have been better, after all.

He looked around, then, to study the rest of his surroundings. But it took him only a moment. His bed, he saw, was
three thick planks, propped together just above the floor.
There was one thin blanket for bedclothing. There was a
half-full water bucket in the corner. There was nothing else.

He sat on the plank bed and took stock of his plight. He
knew that the idleness and the solitude might drive him in-
sane if he surrendered to them. He'd have to find ways of
fighting that danger. He'd have to concentrate on something
—find something to take up his mind or it would fly apart
like a shattered wheel.

And as the weeks passed, he found the outlet for that con-
centration in several small ways. He discovered a loose nail
in his plank bed, and he used it as a pencil when the guard
wasn't watching, or when the thin light of winter was dim
enough to conceal his movements. He composed lines of poetry, and used the nail to scratch them awkwardly and painfully on the stone surface of the floor and the walls. He concentrated on studying the other prisoners during the silent
hour of exercise in the yard. The curve of the shaved skull;
the white-yellow pallor of the flesh, making the face look
corpselike; the brutal eyes of the guards and the lost and
lonely eyes of the convicts. He studied all those things, and
made notes in his mind about them, and he carried the im-
pressions back to his cell where he learned to take them singly
and examine them and compare, as though they were so
many cards in a file.

He concentrated on watching carefully for any small variation in the exercise routine, as though it were critically important that no such variation slip by unnoticed. There

would be the march from the cells, with the prisoners staying fifteen feet apart—twenty men to each gang—three guards to each group. Then into the cheerless dirt yard, single file— walking three times around just inside the walls, always silent, always the same number of steps. Then a turn at the big crank in the center of the yard, to pump water into the prison pipes. He counted the turns, the steps, the motions, to see whether they ever varied from day to day. It gave him something to watch for and to think about later in his cell. And he learned to whisper without moving his lips, so that once in a while he could communicate briefly with another prisoner, going to the crank or coming back inside from the yard.

"How long, mate?"—without a perceptible motion of the stranger's lips.

"Twenty years."

An exchange as brief as that, but something to be carried and prized for days perhaps before it could be taken up again at the next moment of passing within sound.

"How long for you?"—O'Reilly, with his eyes on the ground.

"Till I die."

A conversation completed. Something to work for and look forward to during the endless hours and days and nights.

Then in time, as O'Reilly's mind held firm, they gave him little scraps of work to do in his cell. They let him sew bits of cloth for toweling. They let him untangle snarled twine and roll it into a ball for prison stock. And one morning, through the mercy of some man he never knew, a guard reached sullenly through the iron bars of the door and threw on the floor a copy of *The Imitation of Christ*. O'Reilly knew then that he had conquered Millbank. He had won the fight against madness and in time would move on to another prison, weak in body perhaps but with a mind still clear and healthy.

He wondered about Chambers and McCarthy—how they were standing the terrible test. He longed to share with them some of the comfort he got from reading over and over again the worn pages of the book.

He had no problem now but to wait for his move to some other prison, and to hope meanwhile that, wherever it was, it might be a prison from which he could escape. And so went six months of confinement.

When finally those months were gone, Boyle O'Reilly's despair had turned again to hope. He felt he had survived the worst they could give him. No matter what happened now, someday and somehow he would find his way to freedom. Of that he was convinced. Before long, though, his confidence was weakened.

8. DARTMOOR DRAINS

Boyle O'Reilly had conquered Millbank and the cruel mental punishment of solitary confinement. Even more than that, he had in his own words developed a poignant sort of "fond regard" for some of the associations, born of months of solitude. He wrote about it years later in America, in a quiet hour of remembering:

> One meets strange characters in prison, characters which are at once recognized as being natural to the place, as are bats or owls to a cave. Prison characters, like all others, are seen by different men in different lights.
>
> For instance, a visitor passing along a corridor and glancing through the iron gates or observation holes of the cells, sees only the quiet and—to him—sullen-looking convict, with all the crime-suggesting bumps developed on his shaven head. The same man will be looked upon by the officer who is in charge of him as one of the best, most obedient, and industrious of the prisoners.
>
> No man sees the true nature of the convict but his fellow convict. He looks at him with a level glance and sees him in a common atmosphere. However convicts deceive their prison officers and chaplains, which they do in the majority of cases, they never deceive their fellows.
>
> Some people would think it strange that I should still regard the cell in which I spent solitary confinement with affection. But it is true. Man is a domestic animal, and to a prisoner with 20 YEARS on his door, the cell is Home. I look back with fond regard to a great many cells and a great many prisons.
>
> If ever I should go back to England (which is doubtful),

the first place I would visit would be one of the old prisons. Remember, my name and many a passing thought are scratched and written on many a small place within those cells which I perfectly recollect, and it would be a great treat to go back someday and read them.

And then, during the time I was in prison, I got acquainted with professional criminals, old and young, who will be the occupants of the English jails for the next twenty years. And I confess it would be of great interest to me to go back and walk the corridor with all the brimming respectability of a visitor, and stop when I saw a face I knew of old, and observe how time and villainy had dealt with it.

But a victory over Millbank was not a victory over Dartmoor. Dartmoor was a more brutal and destructive enemy. It was the most terrible prison in all England—a stench-filled, crushing torture machine designed to break a man's body by agonizing labor, purge all sense of hope from his mind, and foul his stomach with food too filthy for the prison pigs.

They sent Boyle O'Reilly there, and at last they nearly broke him—as they had broken thousands of men before him during the years that Dartmoor had hulked over its dark and stagnant Devonshire plain.

He went there as he had gone to Millbank, in clanking chains and suffering the brutal whips and clubs of the guards. He went as though in a group of shackled beasts. Chambers and McCarthy were part of the same sullen lot, and O'Reilly sucked in his breath with horror when he saw how the months behind bars had ravaged them. They could communicate with him only through their eyes, and he longed desperately to be able to whisper to them and perhaps comfort them, if he could, for the pain that had left them with sunken cheeks and thin ribs and the look of trapped animals in their faces. Still, their eyes seemed to brighten when they met his, as though to say they were not yet crushed—they had not yet surrendered to complete despair. There was no chance for anything but the exchange of glances, but it was something that heartened all three.

At Dartmoor he was pushed through a narrow doorway into his new home. He stumbled in, caught his balance, and looked about with dismay. Millbank had been bad, but this was a warning of incredibly harsh days to come. His new cell was built completely of iron—cold, ancient iron. It was seven feet long and four feet wide, with scarcely seven feet of height from floor to ceiling. The only ventilation came through a small two-inch hole at the bottom of the cell door. The only light was the weak and feeble gray shade that came from the dim corridor outside and filtered through a thick piece of glass set in the door.

He discovered that what he had heard was true—that Dartmoor Prison was made to break men's hearts as well as their bodies. It had stood for more than half a century, gloomy and brooding, looking down upon a broad waste of bleak granite hills and murky valleys. For the most part, it stood veiled in mist that rose from the swamps below, or in fog from the sea beyond. It stood silent and sullen, as though searching the depths of its evil heart for new ways to crush a man and to make him long for death.

Through years of dampness and wind its massive stone walls had darkened almost to blackness—a wet blackness from behind which came, irregularly, the melancholy voice of the big prison bell, crying out like a thing forsaken and lost.

Life at Dartmoor was so miserable and harsh that it made Boyle O'Reilly, in a sense, long to return to the more refined cruelties of Millbank. From his first day in the grim place he knew there was little chance of his staying alive through twenty years of such torture. No man could do it, he told

himself. On that day, as on so many that followed, he rolled
from his hard cot at five in the morning, stirred into action
by the clanging of the prison bell and the shouting of the
guards in the corridor. He washed and dressed quickly, and
put his cot in order, for he'd been warned that he'd be
clubbed or whipped if that wasn't done in half an hour.

He was given a hurried few minutes for breakfast. He
watched it being handed into his cell. A single piece of
mouldy bread. A pint of black rye coffee in a battered tin
pail. That was all. He gagged on the bread, and couldn't
force it down. He heard the muttering of a guard behind
him, warning him obscenely that he'd be hungry for worse
things in another few days. O'Reilly had been a prisoner
long enough now to know how little it took to draw a blow
from a guard. He drank the bitter black coffee in silence, and
gulped hard to hold it on his stomach.

Then breakfast was over, and he marched off to work with
the other convicts—long lines of beaten men moving from
their iron cells into the drizzling gray world of Dartmoor
plain, moving down the slope like shuffling corpses, each man
with his hand on the shoulder of the man ahead. Small work
parties were cut off along the way, some to break rocks in the
bleak prison yard, some to work on the massive stone walls
and the high watchtowers.

But on that first day, as on most of those that followed,
Boyle O'Reilly moved along down the slope with a hundred
or so other convicts, to work in the Dartmoor drains. He
knew when he saw the drains that it was hopeless work and
that probably it would never be finished. Below the prison,
at the base of the slope, a vast marshland stretched off to become lost in the foggy distance. For decades the prisoners of
Dartmoor had labored to drain the marsh and reclaim the

land for farming. For decades they had failed, but they were still being forced to try.

French soldiers, captured at Waterloo, had dug long drainage ditches and had died in them. Americans who had been seized in the War of 1812 had built roadways through the swampy land and had fallen dead with their shovels and tools in their hands. Irish rebel prisoners had taken up the work, alongside the criminals of London and Liverpool. Long years of terrible labor had reclaimed ragged patches of land here and there, but had still left a great morass that would keep other convicts occupied for generations to come.

On that morning Boyle O'Reilly walked with the convict line down the sloping inner yard to the lower gate of the prison, then on down the steep road that led from the outside walls to the marshland below.

He could see the deep ditches, wet with dark and stagnant water. He could see the small, scattered patches where the land had been reclaimed, stolen temporarily from the clutch of the swamp. It was sick land, supporting only a few twisted fruit trees and little squares of vegetable plants. It was land that seemed always wreathed in mist, and that might have been a hiding place for lost souls.

He worked that day, for the first of many times, in a drainage ditch that was ten feet deep in the marshland muck and only two feet across at its widest. Standing down there, in stinking water that came almost to his knees, O'Reilly labored with a long-handled spade, cutting wet peat chunks from the bottom and sides of the ditch, somehow swinging them aloft to be seized at the top of the ditch and stacked for drying.

The foul mud and matted grass fell back into his face and mouth and eyes. The slime ran down along his arms and covered his body. It was cruel, inhuman labor. It had been killing men for years, and it would go on killing them for many more years to come. O'Reilly prayed silently as he worked—prayed sometimes for a chance to escape, and sometimes for the sake of Chambers and McCarthy in whatever drainage ditch they might be laboring.

When the storms were too bad, and it was useless to send the men into the drains, Dartmoor had another job for its inmates. O'Reilly discovered that early in his term, on a day when a tempest howled outside the grim prison, and he was taken for the first time to work in the boneshed.

The boneshed ran directly alongside the prison's huge open cesspool. It had a sunken floor and no ventilation. One end was piled high with rotting bones, some of them salvaged from the prison garbage and some of them collected from the countryside around Dartmoor. A day of work in the boneshed meant a day spent breaking the bones and pounding them into dust or jelly. O'Reilly never knew what was done with the putrid product. He knew only that the stench was too much for most prisoners to stand—that many of them stumbled and fell face down in the filth, gagging and retching, only to be whipped to their feet and made to go on working, their faces and stomachs twisting in agony.

He discovered at the start that there was nothing to look forward to in the noontime break. Dartmoor served its big meal at noon, for those who could eat it. At best, it would be bean porridge and old boiled beef, slopped together on a tin plate. At its worst, it would have repelled a hungry jackal. All it accomplished was to add to the ache of starvation and to make a man look forward to supper, hoping that the evening meal would be something better than the bread and bitter coffee of breakfast. But it never was any better; it was always the same.

Soon he was sick with hunger day and night. And soon he was doing as the other convicts did—watching for a chance to escape the eyes of the guards long enough to bite a piece of tallow from a dirty prison candle and chew on it furtively, or to snatch a handful of mud-caked weed roots in the drainage ditch and swallow them quickly when the guards were not looking. Anything that he could keep down—anything that his stomach would not throw back—was far better than the prison food.

And so he weakened and starved, and grew thin and sick. And as he weakened, the guards worked him harder than ever. They clubbed him and shouted at him in the dripping miasma of the drains. They drove him, lurching and vomiting, to spend hours of work in the boneshed, keeping him there until the terrible stench of the place had wrenched from his stomach whatever scraps he'd been able to eat on the sly.

He understood the reasoning behind the treatment. He was a political prisoner, marked for much more cruel handling than the ordinary murderer or bandit. In the eyes of the Crown, no crime was as evil as treason. Therefore, no punishment was too severe and no torture too unspeakable. He accepted it silently, with patience, hoping only that his chance to escape would come before he grew too feeble to make the effort.

Only once did he find a break in the deadly routine of the drains and the boneshed. And even then it was not granted to him with any idea of making his life more comfortable. On the contrary, it was granted with the hope of crushing him still more.

It came about because of a week of steady rains. O'Reilly had spent that week in the boneshed, monotonously pounding away with his mallet at the brittle pieces and the rotting

ones alike. His head ached constantly, from the fumes of the
bone pile and the cesspool. Outside, the rain beat down in
heavy sheets, whipped by gusty winds. He longed and prayed
for the storm to stop, to bring release from the foul shed
and a return to the labor in the swamps.

And finally, one morning, the rain did stop. The guards
shouted an order to halt work on the bones. And O'Reilly
gratefully put aside his mallet and shuffled into line, to move
off toward the prison gate and to return at last to the drainage
trenches.

The sky was a somber gray and the air was still wet when
they stepped outside. A thick fog had settled heavily over
the drains. The dying storm still moaned a bit around the
top of the prison slope. O'Reilly shivered as the damp cold
penetrated his shirt, but he drew great gulps of it into his
lungs. It was like a reprieve, after the long hours with the rotting bones.

The line moved off down the slope and toward the swamp
below. The men stumbled from time to time and tried to
pull themselves upright before drawing the cut of the whip.
They reached the lower gate, and began to file through.

O'Reilly tried to keep his gaze on the heels of the man in
front of him. Usually that helped a prisoner to stay out of
trouble, for it meant that he'd only be doing what the next
man did—moving when he moved, stopping when he
stopped, never drawing a guard's attention by looking
around.

But this day it was different. As threatening and bleak as
the day was, O'Reilly felt better at being outside in the open
air. After a while he forgot about the heels of the man in
front of him, and he raised his head and looked out across
the dripping countryside. A burly guard, walking close alongside, noticed his action and laughed at him viciously.

"Go to it, O'Reilly," he mocked. "Look around all you like. Stare at the muck and the dirt. It's made for the likes of you. Twenty years of it you'll get—but I'm betting you'll die in it first. Look around, O'Reilly!"

But Boyle O'Reilly scarcely heard him. He had seen something that startled him—something he had never noticed before in all the times he'd walked painfully up and down the sloping path. Off to the left, and a few yards below the prison wall, he could see human skulls half-buried in the soil. They seemed to be pushing themselves up from the ground at grotesque angles. He saw grayish-white remnants of skeletons projecting here and there around them.

The guard noticed him staring fixedly at the spot, half-stumbling as he tried to stay in the line without taking his gaze from the hillside. He grumbled at O'Reilly with annoyance.

"What're you staring at, Irishman? Them dirty skulls over there—eh? You'll be no better than them yourself one of these days. And I'm betting it's soon."

O'Reilly stayed silent. He wondered why he'd never noticed them before. Then he realized it was because of the rains. He hadn't seen the skulls before because they hadn't been laid bare before. And then these days of heavy rain had lashed Dartmoor, and had washed great patches of dirt from the side of the slope. And the water rushing downhill had uncovered big granite boulders and slabs of rock—and human skulls. Certainly, that would be it. He wondered where they had come from originally, and what story lay behind them.

Suddenly the guard lunged for him, and grabbed him by the shoulder with a grip that made him want to cry out in pain. He wrenched O'Reilly from the line. The gap closed immediately, man behind man, hand upon shoulder, nobody daring to look up to see what was taking place. O'Reilly lurched and half-fell, then caught himself and straightened up, to wait resignedly for the guard's next move.

"You like skulls, eh?"

O'Reilly kept silent, remembering some of the things that happened to prisoners who spoke without permission.

"Speak up," the guard ordered. "You like skulls, eh?"

O'Reilly looked at the man's coarse face, with its flabby lips and its hungry little eyes. He was puzzled, wondering what was in the guard's mind. Behind him, the gray line of prisoners still shuffled past, moving downhill toward the swamp, paying no attention. O'Reilly decided it was safe to speak—probably safer than keeping silent at the moment.

"I was curious," he said dully. "I never saw them there before."

The guard chuckled. "The rains uncovered them, Irishman. That's why. And d'you know why I pulled you out of line?"

"No, sir." O'Reilly shook his head uneasily.

"To teach you a lesson, Irishman," the guard growled. "To show you what happens to men who think they're better than Englishmen. That's what happens." He waved his hand at the skulls.

It was a grotesque scene, O'Reilly reflected. The bleak moor, the dripping walls of the prison, the low-toned wind, the fog moving across the drains—and now this guard, gesturing at a cluster of half-buried skulls.

The guard placed a heavy hand on O'Reilly's shoulder, as though to hold him there by force and make him look at the bones and listen to the story.

"Those were Americans." The guard spoke with scorn. "They got captured and brought here back in 1812. They tried to mutiny one day. All they had was fists and clubs, but they thought they could beat the English. We turned the guns on them in the main yard, and we shot them down like crazy dogs. They lay there stinking up the main yard worse than the boneshed. So we had the other prisoners dig a big hole down there on the side of the hill and throw the bodies in. Americans!" He spat in the direction of the skulls. "Look at them now!"

But O'Reilly already was looking, and growing angry as he looked. For a herd of prison pigs had come grunting and slipping down the side of the slope, looking for food and scraps in the wet earth. And now the pigs had discovered the skulls, and were rooting up the bones of the dead men, crunching some and trampling others into the loose mud.

The guard was indifferent to the scene. "Any questions, Irishman?" he asked.

O'Reilly wondered if he dared to say what was on his mind. Then he saw two sows, grunting and squealing, rooting together at a rolling skull and slashing at each other for possession of it.

"Yes," he said tightly. "One question."

The guard looked at him as though amused. "What is it, Irishman?"

"I'm asking permission to get a work party together and bury those bones—maybe put stones over the grave, so no animals can dig them out again." He noticed the guard scowl darkly. "After all," he said hurriedly, "if you let the pigs loose, the way the bones are now, there won't be anything left there—and no way of telling the story again."

The guard studied him a moment. Then a slow, crafty smile crossed his lips. "You're right, O'Reilly. We'd better save the bones so we can keep telling the story." He laughed shortly, and the laugh sounded cruel. "So I tell you what, O'Reilly—the job's yours. You just pick out two or three other criminals to help. And then you and them will dig a new grave for the Yankee traitors. A big deep one, too. And then you'll carry heavy stones up this hill from the bottom till you've built a big cairn over the grave and marked what it stands for. And you'd better mark it for Frenchmen, too, because some of them bones come from Napoleon's men.

"And listen, now." He grabbed O'Reilly's shoulder in a painful grip again. "You asked for this job, Irishman. You're going to work hard at it—so hard you'll want to be in the drains again—or even the boneshed. Yes, you'll work so hard there's a good chance you'll die on this job—a real good chance you'll die, O'Reilly."

They dug the grave together—he and Chambers and McCarthy and another imprisoned Fenian, Michael Lavin.

It was punishing labor, for the earth on the slope of the hill was thick with ancient boulders, and the men had been badly weakened by their weeks in the swamp. But none of them felt pain from the work, as they had felt it in the drainage ditches. For somehow, in saving the skulls and bones from the pigs, they felt they were striking a great moral blow at the whole system of despotism and tyranny. They were preserving the dignity of men who had died in much the same cause for which they, too, had fought.

And so the hours of digging through rock-strewn soil, going deeper and deeper into the earth, gave them a feeling of victory that made up for the racking of their bodies. And the long, stumbling climb up the hillside, staggering under the burden of heavy stones, was somehow an easier walk than any they had taken since first reaching Dartmoor.

They had to work in silence, but the frowning guards could not stop them from thinking. O'Reilly knew, as he moved the stones aside with bruised and torn fingers, that the minds of the others were as active as his. And his thoughts were comforting ones. They were thoughts of a young new republic, for which these unknown Americans had offered their lives; and the thought that maybe someday a republic like that would be born in Ireland.

There on the hill above the drains he made up his mind to get to America somehow, if ever he could escape the English chains. He would get to America, he told himself, and learn what it was like to live in brotherhood with men of other religions and other races. He would find listeners there who would hear him tell the story of Ireland and who would help him with the work he and Chambers and McCarthy and all the others had been doing in Dublin. And he, in turn, would learn more about the workings of a free republic, so that the story could be told all the better in Ireland.

Yes, somehow he would have to get to America.

And at last the work was done. All the bones and skulls were placed in the deep new grave, and the dirt was thrown in upon them, and a pyramid of heavy stones raised high above the soil. Then Boyle O'Reilly fastened to the biggest base stone the rough plaque he had made for a marker. It read:

SACRED TO THE MEMORY OF THE
FRENCH AND AMERICAN PRISONERS OF WAR
Who died in Dartmoor Prison
during the years 1811–16.

Dulce et decorum est pro patria mori.
(Erected 1867)

He expected the prison officials to tear down the plaque as soon as they read the inscription. To his surprise, they ignored it. He wondered how long it would remain there and how many other prisoners, reading it, would understand and take heart.

Moving off down the slope that day, going back to the dreaded drains, he took new strength from an unfamiliar feeling of victory. In a way, he told himself, he had won out over Dartmoor even more decisively than he had won over Millbank. He decided he would tell them about this in America someday, if ever he got there.

9. THE HUNTED

AWAKE AT NIGHT, staring into the darkness of his narrow cell, Boyle O'Reilly listened to the familiar noises of the prison—familiar, yet always oppressive and threatening. There was the scrape of a chair at the end of the corridor; the heavy tread of a guard's footstep; the scuttling of a frightened rat; occasionally the faint sound of water; the deep snoring of an exhausted man; the isolated piercing scream of a prisoner whose mind was cracking. He had heard them all many times in the months he had lived in darkness. He could almost, he felt, write a complete and detailed account of life within prison walls at night just by cataloguing and linking each sound that came to him.

But this night he was doing more than listening. He was planning, too—planning patiently for an escape—examining each point of his plan so that nothing could go wrong once he had made his break. He had worked it out carefully, he thought. He had tried to cover every possibility and every situation. And now, awake in the darkness on his hard cot, he decided it would be time soon to make the try. He went over the plan again, point by point, and he could find nothing wrong with it—nothing that might trip him, if he could get just a fair share of luck. It would all depend on the fog, and there was plenty of that around Dartmoor.

For weeks he had developed his plan. He had started by trying to make himself noticed as a model prisoner who obeyed every rule rigidly, no matter how harsh or humiliating it might be. Now, going over it, he checked on the results of that discipline. Yes, they had been good results. The guards frequently were more lax with him than with others. They preferred to pay closer attention to the men who made trouble. And how about the constant searching—the business of having to strip naked four times a day while the guards examined the prisoners' bodies? He was safe on that point, he told himself. The prisoners who had tried to balk at the stripping were still being stripped. And those who had never given trouble were allowed to keep on their prison garb, while the search was reduced to a process of patting and prodding. He was one of those who had not given trouble.

And so, working quietly at night, he had made a rough suit of clothes for himself out of one of the coarse sheets from his bed, and he had rearranged his cot so that the sheet was never missed. He had taken to wearing that rough suit of clothes under his convict's garb, so that he'd be ready to leave his prison uniform behind him instantly if ever the chance came to make the break.

So now there was only the fog to wait for—the fog and the right ditch to be working in, out near the edge of the drains. He had watched the way the guards worked, and he had seen that their routine never changed. When the convicts were in the drains, certain guards were stationed as sentries on the high spots of the bleak moor. They had a double responsibility—to keep an eye on convict gangs and also to keep watch from time to time in the direction of the sea. At the first sign of a heavy fog rolling in from the coast, the sentries would fire their signal guns. The sound of the shots, echoing across the bleak moor, was the signal for the gang guards to round up their workers as quickly as possible, and to start herding them back out of the swamp and up the rock-studded slope to the prison walls.

O'Reilly promised himself that the next time the guns gave the signal of approaching fog would be the instant for him to put his escape plan into action. It was a comforting thought, lying there on the cot in the darkness, listening to the scuttling vermin and the muttering guards and the hacking coughs of the restless prisoners.

Finally the chance came, and Boyle O'Reilly was ready for it. His assignment that day was in a drainage ditch at the far end of the swamp, well beyond the base of the prison slope and close to where a group of rocky knolls rose away from the tangle of muddy weeds.

It was late in the afternoon when the signal came. Working knee-deep in water, at the bottom of his ditch, O'Reilly had spent hours without so much as a glimpse of the earth at ground level. He had no idea what the outlook was like—a threat of rain, a somber mist perhaps, or a deepening twilight. He could not tell, for his only view apart from the high walls of the trench was the opening overhead, two feet wide, where he could see a narrow strip of gray sky. So it had been for hours.

But for hours too, he had been alert for the sound of the guns that would signal the approach of fog. Day after day he had been waiting for that sound. Once or twice the signal had come, but it had found him working in a ditch too close to the prison slope to warrant taking a risk. This day he was in just the right place at just the right time—and suddenly the signal came.

He heard it come booming in, muffled but heavy, from the far side of the moor. Then again from another sentry— and from still another. His heart leaped. A thick, impenetrable fog, rolling in from the sea, cloaking the Devonshire countryside with its cold gray folds. That's what the guns would mean—that and an urgent warning to the gang wardens to round up the convicts in a hurry, for a heavy fog could mean trouble. Overhead he heard the wardens shouting their orders excitedly, herding their gangs together, driving them up from the ditches. Another shot from the signal guns warned them that there was no time to lose.

In O'Reilly's ditch men slogged past him, heavy-footed, bowed with exhaustion, moving mechanically toward the muddy steps that led to ground level at the end of the drain. O'Reilly pressed himself back against the slimy wall and let them go by. They paid him no attention. They were indifferent to anything he was doing. Long ago their spirits had been broken too completely to allow them to take an interest in the actions or plans of any other man. They cared only about staying alive and escaping punishment, and so they moved by like dumb animals, until the last of them had gone.

The fog was coming swiftly. Looking up, he could see its swirling gray hands reaching across the opening of the drain. It would be spreading all across the moor within a few minutes, blotting out the sight of one gang after another, making the swampy plain a blurred world where one man could be indistinct from another at three paces. O'Reilly whispered a prayer of thanks; it was just the kind of fog he needed, and it was sent at just the right hour, with night coming on.

He could see the shadowy figures of the guards, moving about near the top rim of the ditch. He could hear the names of some convicts being called, sharply and insistently. He could hear their dull, mechanical answers. He prayed that his name would not be called. He flattened himself more rigidly against the slime of the wall. Then he heard another shouting of orders, and the clanking of chains, and his heart pounded with excitement. They were moving away, moving like gray ghosts through the thick fog, back toward the slope of the prison hill. And he had not been missed!

He waited only a minute or two, to let them get on their way across the swampland. Then, when everything was silent but the dripping of the fog itself, he moved quickly but quietly to the mud steps at the end of the ditch, and climbed cautiously to the level of the ground.

He looked about him. He could see nothing but the drifting fog swirling across a mound of stacked peat. The air tasted of salt. Night was coming on fast, and the fog was deepening into a grayish black. There was nothing to wait for then. So far there was nobody on the lookout for him. He turned away from the ditch and ran as swiftly and silently as he could across the far edge of the swampland and toward the rocky knolls that he knew lay beyond.

At the edge of the marsh he paused for just a moment. Hastily he stripped off his prison garb. He pushed it down out of sight in the thick mire of a mudhole. Then he straightened up, clad in his cell-made suit, and set out toward the sea.

They didn't discover his escape until the rest of the convicts were back in their cells. By that time he was far away from the prison hill, but he knew the instant the pursuit began. He knew it when he heard the prison bell ringing ominously, carrying across the distance that lay between him and the Dartmoor walls, warning the countryside that a convict was on the loose and should be hunted down like a savage dog.

He stood panting for breath beneath the wet branches of an oak tree, and listened to the bell crying its alarm. The sound of it sent a chill to his heart. Then he turned from the tree and plunged forward into the fog again, praying for the blackness of night to hurry, praying that his trail be lost behind him.

They pursued him for two days and two nights, doggedly and relentlessly. Sometimes in the far distance he could hear their shouts, or the baying of their dogs and the signaling shots of their guns. By day he tried to move in the shelter of woods and lonely paths and rocky hills. By night he moved more freely, striding on hurriedly through the darkness, taking to the roads that he felt would lead him to the seacoast. He wasn't at all sure what he would do when he got there, but he felt certain that somehow he would find release and safety near the edge of the sea.

For two days and two nights he ate nothing at all. He dared not beg for food at a farmhouse, or run the risk of getting caught while trying to steal. And for two days and two nights he scarcely slept, trying desperately to stay ahead of the distant sound of dogs and men, afraid to lie down defenseless and risk falling into a sleep that would end in his capture.

On the second night they were closing in. O'Reilly was exhausted, almost at the point of collapse. His flight had become a staggering, lurching nightmare. His clothing was ragged and torn, ripped by briars and rocks and branches that had caught at him as he stumbled past. His hands and legs were cut and bruised and bleeding. His eyes were bright and almost feverish, with the desperate fear of being overtaken and the dogged instinct to keep plunging on as long as he could summon any strength at all.

And on that night he heard them close behind him as he limped hurriedly along a dirt road at the edge of a little village. He heard the dogs again, and the voices of the guards, this time loud and close at hand. His heart seemed to cry out in despair. He had been so close to freedom!—so close!

In desperation he made one more try to shake them off. It was a misty night, and the dogs must long since have lost his scent on the wet roadway. His pursuers had nothing to go on then, except the possibility that he had passed this way.

Just up ahead, through the darkness, he saw the outlines of

a small cottage. He saw a shed at the back, standing close to the edge of the roof. He felt a sudden surge of hope again, and he padded forward quickly, keeping to the side of the road and trying to blend his shadow with the darkness of the trees. He slipped from the roadway into the back yard of the house, hoping there'd be no dog around to bark an alarm. Everything was silent, except for the sound of the voices, coming closer from down the road. Quickly he pulled himself to the top of the shed, climbed from there to the cottage roof, and edged himself into the shelter of the chimney shadow.

Within a minute or two the guards had reached the cottage and were thumping at the door. O'Reilly crouched just a few feet above them. He heard the dogs in the yard, sniffing and panting noisily. He heard the men swearing and arguing among themselves as they pounded at the door again. There was nobody in the cottage. Two of the men took a quick look around the yard. O'Reilly heard one of them whistle for the dogs. Then he saw them moving off through the night, still following the road toward the center of the village.

He slipped down quickly, and doubled back up the road in the direction from which he had come. But he had reached the end. He was weary, beaten, and sick. He no longer knew where he was heading or what he hoped to do when he got there. He was nothing now but a torn and bleeding prey, moving awkwardly, sometimes falling to his knees, sometimes walking blindly into briar thickets or lurching openly down the middle of the road.

He came to the edge of a river without knowing or caring what river it was or where it led. Again, as on that same night earlier, he could hear the sound of men and dogs behind him, closing in, growing louder and nearer. He gave himself up to dry sobs, and he stared at the dark water of the river as it flowed slowly along just below his feet. It would be so easy, he felt, to lose himself in that water, or to stop his flight with a final grasp at life, and to surrender to the guards. He could hear them close at hand now—could even hear the heavy panting of the dogs, just beyond a nearby clump of bushes.

But always there should be one more try. Always one more clutch at freedom, no matter how hopeless it seemed. His mind rejected any other thought.

He eased himself gently into the river, feeling it wrap coolly and soothingly around him, careful not to disturb the water any more than he could help. The men were close at hand now, standing on the riverbank just above his head. He moved softly in beneath the overhang of the bank. He kept his head barely above water there, holding himself in the shadows, clinging with one hand to the stump of a willow branch. He waited, scarcely daring to breathe.

Above, he heard the guards spread out and start walking slowly, searchingly, through the tall grass and underbrush along the river's edge. They talked quietly among themselves, not hurrying, not excited, confident that in the end they would capture him, either here or wherever else they might overtake him. Once or twice he heard them mention his name, and in his dazed condition he couldn't decide whether they were calling him or talking about him. Then he heard one of them speak about a ripple on the water—a strange ripple, it seemed, at a place where no ripple should be showing. He wondered about that—wondered what they meant. And as he thought about it, he heard their steps coming back again to the riverbank above his head. And he saw with despair that the strange ripple they spoke about was being made by the water flowing over his body.

"O'Reilly!" One of them spoke his name.

Then two of them slipped down from the grass, landing

with a splash in the water beside him. They reached in under the bank, each taking one of his arms, and they pulled him out of his hiding place.

He gave a sob of surrender, and collapsed unconscious in their grip.

10. FROM CHAINS TO CANVAS

THE FALL of the year came around again. It brought to Dartmoor the cold autumn rains and a constant damp chill that filled the prison corridors. Boyle O'Reilly sat in his iron cell, in the gray half-light of dawn, and thought back on the months just gone. It was barely more than a year since he'd been marched in chains through Dublin. Yet it seemed like half a lifetime. It seemed another age entirely when he and Chambers and McCarthy had stood on the parade ground at the Royal Barracks, waiting resignedly to be stripped of their uniforms.

He hoped he would find the strength, somehow, to live through the coming winter. It would be very hard, for Dartmoor had beaten him down steadily and brutally and relentlessly. His body now was little more than a gaunt frame of bones and skin. And what alarmed him most was that it seemed like a terrible effort to do the simplest thing. Even sitting in his cell in the chill minutes of dawn, it was an effort just to lift his ice-cold fingers to his mouth and breathe upon them for warmth.

What strength he'd had left had been wasted on the escape that failed. It had drained from him at last in the flight through the fog and in the exhaustion of being hunted and chased and caught, with no food in his stomach for two frightening days and nights.

Then, when they'd brought him back to Dartmoor, they'd thrown him into solitary confinement for four weeks, and had kept him alive on bread and water. When at last they'd returned him to his cell, he'd been scarcely more than a caricature of a man—an awkward body with the skin drawn tight over the bones, with hollows where the flesh should have been firm. And so he'd remained, unable to gain back his strength or his weight on the repulsive food of the prison.

Now it was autumn again, and he prayed to live through the coming winter. For the dream of freedom was still alive. They had robbed him of health and dignity and laughter. They had left him sickness and degradation and bitter loneliness. But they had not been able to take away the dream.

It was that night, after another agonizing day in the drains, that he heard the news that struck a spark of fresh hope and excitement in his heart. He never was certain how the story had spread, how it reached his ears. It moved through the prison in that strange way peculiar to prison rumors. There was no source and no apparent passing of words from any one man to another. And yet there was a story going around—a report that moved elusively through the prison and penetrated to the darkest corners of the corridors and cells.

A convict ship was sailing for Australia, and there'd be men from Dartmoor sailing with her! Somehow the news reached Boyle O'Reilly. He lay on his cot in the darkness, excited and yet almost afraid to hope. It would mean a new life, new chances for escape, new fire for the old dreams. Whatever the punishments and hardships might be, either aboard ship or in Australia, they'd still mean release from Dartmoor. Some convicts would be sailing. If only he might be one of the lot! If only he might go! He lay, holding the thought close to him, and he prayed and hoped and wondered.

And the next night, while the excitement within him was still fresh, he heard them coming down the corridor toward his cell. He heard the footsteps of the guards echoing along the iron walls, and he heard the rattling of keys and the opening and clanging of cell doors. God! he thought, don't let them stop! Keep them coming to me! Keep them coming to me!

The sounds drew closer, and he shook violently, racked by the suspense and the tension. He had to fight down an impulse to cry out to the guards and plead with them to come and take him away. Then, suddenly, he heard the footsteps stop outside his cell. The dim yellow light of a lantern filtered in through the peephole. He heard a heavy key grate in the lock, and then the door swung open and the lantern glow cast tall shadows along the cell walls.

One of the guards gestured to him brusquely.

"Get up, O'Reilly. You're leavin'."

He rose shakily to his feet. He weaved and sagged a little as the guards caught his arms and swore at him.

"On your way, Irishman!" They pushed him forward roughly, through the door and into the cold corridor.

His mind was blurred with the excitement and the shock of relief. Never again to see Dartmoor! Never again the bleak moor, the prison pigs, the drains, or the stench of the bone shed. He'd be going away to another land, far away to the end of the earth, perhaps never again to see Ireland or the friends he loved—but never again to see the prisons of England, either. And perhaps, someday, somehow, there'd be America.

They went chained together, twenty of them from Dartmoor's darkest cells—chained with double irons on their arms. O'Reilly looked hopefully for Chambers or McCarthy in the group, but they were not there.

That night there was a long ride on the railroad, in a special car marked for Portland. They went northeast, around the head of Lyme Bay, and then south down the narrow peninsula to the harbor town.

It was a grisly, unreal journey—a journey that meant trag-

edy for some and a weak flame of hope for others. It was a
ghostly journey, made in a setting of wavering lantern light
and strange sounds, of Devon villages slipping by in the darkness, and of unspoken thoughts that were heavy on the air.

It was late at night when finally they reached Portland.
O'Reilly was prodded from the train, and immediately felt
braced by the seacoast air. His nostrils caught the scent of salt
and tar and rope, blending in the darkness into the timeless
smell of all harbor towns. He could hear the creaking of
masts and spars, the slatting of lines, and from somewhere
out across the water the distant sound of a channel bell. It
seemed like a wonderful release, after the deadening nights
of Millbank and Dartmoor.

They were driven quickly from the railroad to the receiv-
ing prison, and there they were grouped together in a room
of cold bare stone. Their irons were unlocked, and their
chains dropped to the floor with a loud, jangling rattle. A
guard with a thick club in his hand poked them back from
the chains, jabbing them in the ribs, making them stand in
a grotesque line against the wall.

"Everybody strip!" he shouted at them. "Everything off!
All your clothes go back to Dartmoor. You'll get fresh uniforms here."

Boyle O'Reilly gladly shed the hated Dartmoor garb, and
then he folded it carefully, to be collected with the others.
He wondered vaguely who'd be the next man to wear his
clothes, and to shiver in them while working in the drains.
He stepped back naked, standing rigid against the wall, waiting submissively to be told what to do next. They stood that
way, twenty of them, bare and motionless and silent, while
prison guards came and went on other business and paid
them no attention except to jeer at them occasionally and
ridicule their scrawny flanks and their bony joints.

It was two hours before the guards got around to bringing them any fresh clothing. Meanwhile, they stood silent and submissive and cold, until at last they were led off one by one to cells that were so much like all the other cells they had known.

And then, after a week of days that dragged, they were routed out abruptly late one afternoon and ordered to Portland Prison yard. The sun was low in the sky, and the yard was chill and forbidding with the approach of twilight; but even so, Boyle O'Reilly felt a surge of excitement and hope as he moved through the prison's inner door. This, now, could mean only one thing. It could mean only that the waiting was over and all the prisoners had reached Portland from the distant corners of England, and it was time to go aboard the convict ship. It was time at last to be moving toward some sort of action again, however hidden its nature might be.

He looked around as he stepped into the yard, and he saw that strangers had arrived—other convicts from other cells, some of them looking frightened as though prison life were new and unfamiliar to them, others looking gaunt and furtive with all the marks and signs of many months of confinement.

And close by, in the area next to O'Reilly and the Dartmoor group, he recognized the faces of men he had known in Ireland. They exchanged glances, and he noticed that some of them looked shocked and startled at his appearance, and he saw a light of sympathy come into their eyes. They must have been newly arrested and convicted, he observed, or they'd have learned before now what prison life could do to a man. He felt sorry for them, thinking of the suffering and disillusion and pain that lay ahead of them.

The guards were shouting orders, barking at them as though in a military camp.

"Fall in there! Shoulders back! Fall in there!"

O'Reilly took his place in line, thinking how ludicrous it all seemed. He'd have felt more at ease, he told himself, with the clubs and whips of Dartmoor at his shoulders. It was contemptible to be injecting a military air into such a shameful spectacle.

He heard the clanking of chains, somewhere off to the left. And then they were all shackled once more in the familiar old style, familiar and yet shocking no matter how many times it happened. Double irons for the arms again. Double irons and heavy chains. They were linked together in groups of twenty, with the political prisoners in shackles of their own and the common criminals in others. Then came the military command:

"Forward, march!"

The prisoners trooped, dragging and clanking, out to the esplanade of the prison. There they wheeled right and marched off in a mockery of smart drill. O'Reilly sucked in his breath as he saw what was happening. It was incredible! It was terrible, idiotic and incredible! The convicts were being marched in a sickening sort of military review, being led on parade past the prison governor and the officers of the convict ship.

He thought back quickly to the brilliant reviews of the Tenth Hussars and the other fine troops in Dublin, and he wanted to retch at the sight of this travesty and the fact that he was forced to take a part in it. It was the same old story, the thing he'd been fighting against for such a long and painful time—the abuse of power and the malicious use of authority in ways that might crush a man's spirit and dignity.

Marching past the review point, he cast a quick side glance at a group of tanned sailors standing behind the ship's officers. He read the name on their caps: *Hougoumont*. He had heard tales of that ship, picked up here and there in the years gone by. She was sturdy and fast, and a good seagoing craft, but she was a hell ship, too, with the bloodstains of many men on her decks and the ghosts of others swinging from her yardarms. Still—he shrugged mentally—she was a means of leaving England. She was his transportation to a new kind of life, with new chances for escape, and perhaps even new hope of staying alive.

The last of the long line clanked past the reviewing stand, and the military farce was ended. The convicts were reformed again in their columns of chains. The guards shouted their orders. And the prisoners started off on their march to the water front, to board a harbor craft and be ferried out to the *Hougoumont*.

And broken hearts went with them, on their way to the edge of the harbor. Spectators lined the street, looking hopefully and desperately into the faces of the men who passed by, seeking a husband, a brother, a son. Some of them ran alongside, going quickly up and down the line, the women clutching the arm of a prisoner here and there, searching frantically for a loved one, or for someone who might have news of his whereabouts.

The guards paid little attention to the cruel drama. They ignored the screams that sometimes came when a wife would find her husband, and would throw herself upon him, half-insane in her grief and despair. The line slogged on relentlessly. The chains clanked and jangled. The women, stumbling along the line, wept and cried out.

O'Reilly walked at the rear of the column, chained to other political prisoners. From his place at the end he could see all that was taking place, and his heart was heavy for the suffering and the tears. Then, oddly enough, he heard his own name being called.

"O'Reilly! Boyle O'Reilly!—here!"

It came from the sidewalk, not loud enough to attract the guards, in case they'd want to interfere. O'Reilly glanced over curiously. He couldn't think of anyone he knew in Portland. He saw a little man in a black coat staring at him questioningly, edging along through the crowd.

"O'Reilly?" The man was looking straight at him.

O'Reilly nodded his head; he didn't know the stranger.

The little man hurried from the side of the street and fell into a quick step beside him. He spoke furtively.

"I was told to look for you—about your brother Will."

O'Reilly's heart leaped. "What about him, man? Quick, what about him?"

"Arrested in Dublin. Sends his love—says to fight on." The little man began to edge away.

"Wait!" O'Reilly pleaded. "What——?"

"Can't wait," the little man said. "We were Fenians together. They got Will—they're looking for me. Good luck to you!"

He darted back to the crowd at the edge of the street and quickly disappeared. O'Reilly tried to see where he had gone, but the line moved on and it was hopeless to search the crowd any longer. So they'd arrested Will, too, and made him another in the long list of political prisoners. Millbank and solitary confinement, probably. Chatham and the brickyard. Dartmoor and the drains and the boneshed. O'Reilly's heart was sad. And yet at the same time it seemed to pick up courage at the thought that no matter how many men were punished or killed, there would always be friends and brothers moving up to take their places and to carry on the work. Someday, then, it would succeed. Not only in Ireland, but in all other lands.

He was smiling with that thought as he went aboard the harbor craft for the ride out to where the *Hougoumont* lay at anchor.

11. THE WILD GOOSE

DAY BY DAY the *Hougoumont* plunged through the autumn storms of the North Atlantic, carrying her hideous cargo southward. England lay far behind now, lost to sight somewhere beyond the scudding clouds that blurred the northern horizon. And Ireland seemed still farther distant, obscured by the tears and the painful memories of the exiles.

The ship beat steadily to the south. Off the Bay of Biscay gale winds whipped at her rigging and piled great frothing waves against her bow. At times she rolled heavily, struggling to make headway. At other times, with a change of course, she cut swiftly through the foam, driven by the shrieking wind on her quarter and the rush of a following sea. By day the clouds were always gray, always hurrying, always ragged. By night the wind made the rigging whine and hurled stinging spray across the decks. The cold rains beat down. The ship rolled and plunged and strained. The convicts cursed and screamed and howled.

Boyle O'Reilly listened to the din, lying awake in the darkness where his hammock was slung beneath a shelter on the lower deck. He was restless and uneasy, acutely aware of the misery that existed all about him. Still, there was nothing he could do to help ease it. Compared to some of the wretches aboard, his own lot was an easy one. But there was no way he could share it. And he'd been a convict long enough now to realize that one had to be practical to stay alive and sane— that he had to accept whatever came his way, taking the occasional bit of good to pay for the many hours of misery.

In his case, life had improved almost from the instant he'd stepped aboard the *Hougoumont*. On that first night in Portland Harbor he had recoiled from the stark horror of the convict ship. The prisoners' chains were knocked off on deck, and the men were ordered to go below. On his way down the main hatchway he'd shuddered at the twisting faces that looked out from behind iron bars, searching the eyes of the newcomers, crying out in voices that were half-mad, half-derisive.

He had entered the forward hold, and tried to adjust his eyes to the sickly shadows cast by the light of the ship's lamps. He had looked with stunned shock at the mass of men confined in there—more than three hundred of them, murderers and rapists and thugs, the reeking overflow of England's worst criminal cesspools. They had shrieked a hideous, diabolical welcome to the newcomers, a fierce din of shouts and shrill curses and piercing laughter. And then he had felt a stranger take his arm and whisper, "Come—we are waiting for you." And he'd been led through the raging crowd of criminals to a door amidships and into a small room that a group of convicted Fenian soldiers had claimed for themselves. He became one of the group.

For him, then, the shipboard life was never as bad as it might have been. Among the military guards there were several soldiers who had belonged to the same regiments that had been garrisoned in Dublin—the Highlanders, the Light Infantry, even one or two who had once served with the Tenth Hussars. And they allowed O'Reilly and the Fenians to use the quarters they had claimed during the day and to sling their hammocks under a shelter deck at night. Otherwise, he realized, he would have been caged in the forward hold with the criminal mob, where the air was noisome, and the din was like an echo from hell, and the deck was foul with the vomit of seasick prisoners and the filth of overturned slop pails.

League after league the *Hougoumont* rolled southward, until at last the North Atlantic storms lay far astern of her foaming wake. The North Star dropped ever closer to the horizon behind them, and finally disappeared. Ahead, the Southern Cross rose in the sky. The southern trades blew steadily, and the ship moved into warm latitudes and quiet seas.

Sometimes at night, when land was just below the horizon off to port, Boyle O'Reilly thought he could detect a strange scent that was borne out across the waves by an offshore breeze. It held a hint of spice about it, and a hint of old age and decay, and he thought to himself that the coast of Africa must lie off in that direction, just beyond sight. And sometimes by day, as they kept moving south, land birds that were unknown to him would settle briefly on the *Hougoumont's* spars and rigging before flying off out of sight, toward islands that he could not see.

The sun grew warm, and the sea grew flat, and a steady wind pushed them ever south, ever south. But the calm of the sea and the soft heat of the air were not enough to make it a quiet voyage. At times the ship seemed almost to shudder, as though to shake off the noises of hell. At the slightest provocation the criminals shrieked and cursed, fought and howled, screamed with madness and fury and despair, sometimes at high noon and sometimes frighteningly in the darkest hours of the night.

Day after day there was always a line of victims for the morning floggings. Day after day O'Reilly saw men cut and slashed and bruised by the vicious whips. And for those who lived through the floggings and still rebelled there was always the halter. This was a length of rope suspended from the foreyard, used to send mutineers and murderers swinging out over the sea, to dangle there in agony until they died.

O'Reilly and the other Fenians escaped the tortures and killings. They stayed by themselves, under the discipline of the military guards, and they were careful to obey all the rules and to stay clear of the punishment cage.

Their behavior won them occasional concessions—a few special liberties, small at first but increasingly better as the voyage went along. That, thought O'Reilly, was the only sensible way to act. It couldn't possibly do any good to cause trouble aboard ship. There'd be time enough to plan an escape and break the rules when the journey was over.

Before long the wardens listened to his request for permission to put out a shipboard paper, and they gave him the materials to work with, after warning him against writing anything that might cause trouble.

Thus was born on the *Hougoumont* a weekly publication that O'Reilly named *The Wild Goose*. He chose the name with a thought for the Irish soldiers of another day who had fled their own land to serve in the armies of France and other countries, exiled forever from their homes. As a little boy he had heard his father tell stories of the "Wild Geese" and why they never could return to Ireland. He felt, now, that there couldn't be any more fitting name for his paper.

The Wild Goose appeared aboard ship every Saturday for seven weeks. O'Reilly did the editing. Two other Fenians— John Flood and J. Edward O'Kelly—helped him with the writing. And still another, Denis B. Cashman, sketched the pictures and the title line, sprinkling his work liberally with shamrocks.

The paper was an immediate success. Each Sunday night O'Reilly was allowed to group all the Irish prisoners below decks in the shadows of the hold and to read them what had

been written. They'd sit around in a silent semicircle, with
the dim yellow glow of a ship's lantern throwing a weird light
on their faces, and they'd listen in silence but with eager eyes
as he read them the stories of Irish deeds and the warm descriptions of the towns and valleys and hills they remembered
so well—and probably never again would see.

It was in *The Wild Goose*—as the *Hougoumont* was
rounding the Cape of Good Hope—that he first put down
his poem "The Flying Dutchman," with its poignant closing
lines:

> They'll never reach their destined port—they'll
>   see their homes no more—
> They who see the Flying Dutchman—never, never
>   reach the shore!

The ship rounded the tip of Africa, and began the long
reach eastward, across the Indian Ocean toward Australia.
Somewhere ahead lay Fremantle, and the bars and cells of
another prison, and fierce, hot days of jungle labor. But somewhere ahead, too, lay the possibility of another chance at escape—another break for freedom, and the chance to find a
new home. Even aboard a hell ship the thought of that was a
comforting thing during the long, weary weeks, and a sooth-
ing thing in the lonely hours of night.

And, as they sailed on, each night Boyle O'Reilly secretly
led the Irish exiles in prayer. Catholic and Protestants alike,
they knelt with him and offered their plea, while the ship
rolled gently and the lantern light played on their bared
heads:

> O God, who art the arbiter of the destiny of nations, and
> who rulest the world in Thy great wisdom, look down, we
> beseech Thee, from Thy holy place, on the sufferings of our
> poor country. Scatter her enemies, O Lord, and confound

their evil projects. Hear us, O God, hear the earnest cry of our people, and give them strength and fortitude to dare and suffer in Thy holy cause. Send her help, O Lord, from Thy holy place. Amen!

They drew strength from that prayer, and a sense of being less lonely, less despairing, and somehow less uncertain of their future. Then, too, they felt that their prayers were helping Ireland.

12. DOWN UNDER

THE PRISONERS went ashore at Fremantle in the steaming sultry heat of an early January morning. They stood at the harbor's edge with their chains still hanging, and they listened to the rasping voice of a guard as he read the rules of the prison colony and the punishments for breaking those rules.

". . . the penalty for which is death . . . the penalty for which is death . . . the penalty for which is death. . . ."

Over and over came the same warning, until its effectiveness was smothered by monotonous repetition. Finally the guard droned to the end of his paper and the convicts picked up their chains again and shuffled off up the slope toward the big white stone prison that looked down gloomily on the little town and the thickly wooded countryside.

Boyle O'Reilly glanced back briefly. He saw the *Hougoumont* swaying gently at her anchor line. Her sails were furled and the light of the rising sun shone with stark, clean brilliance on her spars and masts and empty deck. Seeing her there in the brightening of the morning, it was hard to think of her as a hell ship with a hideous, repulsive cargo. A sailing vessel was a thing to love and remember, for her graceful lines and the white of her canvas and the brave, reckless freedom she should represent. This ship, though, he loathed, for she represented tyranny and despotism at their worst. It was criminal to let her ride the waves and challenge the wind, for she was an instrument of man's cruelty and madness and despair.

He turned away, hating the sight of her, and he walked on

up the slope behind his chained companions. He rubbed a gathering of sweat from his forehead, and scowled uneasily at the rising sun. It was going to be torture, working in this land, fighting the heat and the humid air along with all the usual nagging torments of prison life.

The line moved in through the prison yard, and one by one the convicts were cut from their chain groups like heads of cattle cut from a herd. And one by one the iron-barred doors slammed closed behind them, penning them in their cells.

They left O'Reilly alone for a long time that first day, for the arrival of a shipload of prisoners always meant hours of poring over records in the prison office. Political criminals had to be separated from common criminals, murderers from mutineers, soldiers from civilians, and papers had to be made out for the work assignments of each one. Labor gangs had to be made up on paper, to be grouped together and shipped out the following day, the milder prisoners to be sent to the stone quarries at Perth some twenty miles away, the murderers and ex-soldiers to be sent south to join the road gangs in the distant jungle of the Vasse.

O'Reilly listened to their footsteps coming and going and to the occasional clanging slam of a door. And he sat quietly but impatiently, eager to get started on his own assignment, for the sooner he reached his work gang the sooner he could start planning his escape. It might take years, but meanwhile each minute seemed a precious thing that was going to waste.

It was late afternoon before they sent for him. He heard their steps approaching his cell, two guards talking in low tones as they came. And he rose quickly to be ready for them, and to get started on his next journey, wherever it might lead. But they had not come to take him from the prison.

"O'Reilly!" They pulled the heavy door open and beckoned to him. One guard tossed him his new uniform—white canvas trousers, blue woolen shirt, a broad-brimmed white hat. "Put those on. Leave the rest of your things folded on the cot."

O'Reilly did as he was told, silently, while the guards lounged in the open doorway of the cell. He thought, standing naked and reaching for the white trousers, how different it was from Dartmoor or Millbank. The air was hot here, but it didn't reek. The guards were alert and hostile, but so far at least nobody had clubbed or kicked him. It was much better than a drainage ditch; that was something to be thankful for. He knotted the cord at the top of his trousers, and stood waiting for the next order.

"Follow us."

They went out through the corridor, past rows of cells where some men lay weeping and others stood muttering oaths under their breath, and still others sat motionless, staring ahead as though numbed. And finally they came to a paneled door marked "Library." One of the guards knocked.

"Open!" The response from within was quick. The voice was heavy, strong.

The guards opened the door and pushed O'Reilly inside.

"Here he is, Father. You're to take him back when you're done."

"Thank you. He'll be all right. Just leave us undisturbed."

The guards stepped back, and shut the door behind them.

Boyle O'Reilly stood there bewildered, staring at the priest who sat facing him. He saw a big man with thick white hair, a man with skin that had sun-baked to a dark brown. He was in his shirt sleeves, and there was a scar on one of his corded forearms. He sat behind a littered desk, with his hands clasped together at the back of his neck. His eyes were gray and sharp, and they traveled quickly up and down O'Reilly, and then they brightened as he nodded. He stood up and came from behind the desk, and looked down at O'Reilly and held out his hand.

"I'm Father Lynch—the Catholic chaplain here." His grip was strong.

O'Reilly looked down, wordless and confused, as the handshake broke. It was so long since any man had welcomed him. He looked up again, wondering, in silence.

"It's all right," Father Lynch said. "You can talk here. This isn't Dartmoor. It has its bad points, but it isn't Dartmoor. Here—sit down." He gestured at a deep leather chair beside the desk, and guided O'Reilly toward it. Then he went behind the desk again to his own chair. "Look around. What do you think of our prison library? Take a good look." He was obviously giving O'Reilly a chance to recover and feel at ease before expecting him to speak.

O'Reilly was puzzled. He looked around. He saw that it was a small room, but there was good light through the windows and there was space to move about. There were shelves of books along the wall. Most of the volumes looked worn through age rather than through use. There were three or four tables with straight chairs, a yellowed wall clock that ticked slowly, a picture of the Queen with a small British flag hanging in dusty folds above it. A fly was buzzing lazily in one corner of the ceiling, and bumping itself against a rolled window shade.

He looked back at Father Lynch and smiled briefly. "Compared to a cell, it's like a wing in a mansion."

"You look the way I'd expected," Father Lynch said, keeping his eyes on O'Reilly's face. He nodded. "Thin but not sick—young and hardened—resigned to discipline, but not to defeat."

"The way you'd expected——?"

"Yes. I've been waiting for you. It was a slow voyage, wasn't it?"

"Waiting for me?"

The priest chuckled. "One thing, though. I'd heard you had a brilliant tongue. So far, you've sounded like a parrot."

O'Reilly shrugged helplessly. "So many months, Father. I learned not to talk. A club is persuasive. And after so many months, suddenly a handshake and a kind voice. And I don't know why, so what can I say?"

"I was joking," the priest said gently. "I only wanted to put you at ease. You're safe here. Feel free to talk and say anything you like. You're in my hands now, for a time—till they send you down the coast to the jungle."

O'Reilly discovered he was gripping the arms of his chair. He let his hands go loose. "I believe you, Father. I don't know why I'm here or what you know about me or what it's all about, but I'll enjoy it for as long as it lasts. I'll just sit and listen. It's very pleasant—after so long."

"That's better. Forget the tension while you're here." The priest glanced at the clock, and pulled open his desk drawer. "Library hours are over for the day. Here—smoke a cigar with me."

A cigar! Boyle O'Reilly coughed and gasped when the smoke first hit his lungs. He felt the tears sting his eyes. He'd almost forgotten what tobacco was like. Father Lynch paid no attention to his spasms, but leaned back in his chair and smoked comfortably as he talked. And after a while O'Reilly grew more and more at ease until he, too, was leaning back in his chair, enjoying his cigar, and listening to the priest's story. The man's heavy voice droned—at times rough, at times almost musical.

"Yes, I know all about you—all that's important, anyhow. The word came along weeks ago that you were on your way.

After you've been here a while you'll understand how that can happen—how the word can get from one Irishman to another, halfway around the world, when it's something that concerns Ireland. I hear many stories that way. I never question them too deeply—just accept them when they reach me.

"In your case, I know your father was a teacher. I know of your home at Dowth Castle. I know how you joined the Tenth Hussars and worked with John Devoy and the other Fenians—and about your trial, and all.

"I know things that probably you don't know yourself. Your mother is quite ill. Had you heard that? I thought not. Your brother Will was convicted and sent to Millbank. Poor man—he hasn't the physical strength that you had. It may go hard with him there. Your friends Chambers and McCarthy are still at Dartmoor, and there's not a chance they'll ever be sent to any other place. It doesn't go well with them at all.

"The Fenians want me to help you. They feel you'll be free someday—that you'll do great things for Ireland. They want me to take you on here—let you work as my assistant in the library. I've needed an assistant for some weeks now—the last man that was here took ill and died. When I heard of your record, I agreed to take you. You're the kind of man I want —one who loves books and mankind—who has kept his honor and his courage. One who'll always dream the dream of Ireland while knowing he may never see the green hills again.

"You'll not be here long, for they're sending you south to the jungle—to the mahogany forest. But while you're here, you'll be free—as free, that is, as a man can be and still live in a prison. We'll talk a lot, you and I—and perhaps some of the things we'll be talking about may help you in the future.

"I know you'll be hoping to escape. But down there where the mahogany grows it's almost useless to try. The Bush is terribly thick, O'Reilly—almost impossible to break through. A man can take five steps into it and be lost forever and die there. And if by some miracle he does push on through, he comes to the endless ocean or the empty desert. Then there's no going ahead—just a turning back for punishment, or a waiting for slow death. But I know you'll be planning and hoping, and we'll be talking about that some of the time, too.

"Here in Fremantle they'll probably let me take you out to walk, or to ride around at times—on prison business, of course. You'll find it a strange place. It's beautiful in some ways and terrible in others. You'll see Swan River, where it flows into the sea—its clear water and brown stones and white sand. You'll see the black swans that live there and give it the name. You'll want to write poetry about it all.

"Then, about a mile up the river, there's a great gloomy cliff that juts out over the water and glowers down. The Fremantle stone quarries are there, and the chain gangs that work them. And sometimes there'll be a man leap from the cliff to the water below, thinking he can swim to freedom with irons on his feet. Nobody ever has escaped that way. The poor wretches sink, and there's no more said about them.

"Farther up, about ten miles, I'd say, the river winds among the low hills and the green valleys, and it's very beautiful there. You'll see black women and children sitting quietly on the rocks, watching the head of the family spearing fish for dinner. You'll like the natives, O'Reilly. Being savages, they haven't had a chance to learn the trickeries and deceits of the civilized white men. They're very happy and very honest, and very close to the God we love and Whom they haven't even heard about.

"You'll see kangaroos nibbling the grass at the river's edge, and beautiful snakes swimming in the water. You'll see the big stone quarries at Perth, and more chain gangs. You'll see the gentle Sisters of Mercy and their convent school on the riverbank."

Boyle O'Reilly listened to it all in a haze of pleasure. He smoked his cigar, and felt the pangs of months of torture easing away, and he knew he would enjoy his work with Father Lynch and would recapture some of his sense of beauty and peace, so badly torn by prison life.

"And so," the priest was concluding, "that's about what it will be like for the short time they let you stay with me. And now, if you like, ask all the questions you care to, and I'll try to answer them with what I know. About your family and your friends and anything—though there'll be a great lot I'll not be able to answer. A great lot, indeed.

"And then when you've asked the questions—then, tell me about Ireland. Tell of the salmon in the Corrib River and the green slope of Tara and the pubs of Dublin. I'm hungry to hear of it all. It's been a great many years, O'Reilly, a great many years, since I've been home.

"But first, though, before you ask me the questions or start talking of the old country, tell me one thing. What do you plan as a prisoner here in Australia?"

O'Reilly smiled at him through the cigar smoke. "Just what you're thinking, Father. I've only one plan. Freedom."

13. DESIGN FOR FREEDOM

I T LASTED only a short time, his work in the prison library
at Fremantle. But while it lasted, it was like a torrent of
clear, cold water to a man who'd been dying of thirst, or
like a burst of sun and fresh air to a man who'd been penned
in a dungeon.

Books again, after months of literary famine! He read
avidly, and there was so much to read that at first his mind
kept stumbling in its haste to absorb all it could while the
books were at hand. It was as though he expected somebody
to rush in and snatch them away.

Poetry again, and he thought back on the fragments of
lines he had scratched on the walls of cells at Millbank and
Chatham and Dartmoor. Now he could read if he chose, or
write if he chose.

And newspapers again, old in date but new to him. It was
two years since he'd seen a newspaper. He could find no papers from Ireland, but he found many old copies from America, and he carried them all aside to a sunlit corner of the
library and arranged them in order and went through them
one by one, learning of all that had been happening in the
world.

He read of how the United States was recovering, mending
its wounds, putting itself back together after its savage war.
He learned about carpetbaggers and copperheads, about
newly freed Negroes floundering around in pathetic attempts
to catch up with civilization, about the people themselves
doggedly putting a young country back on its feet and writing their own new laws to keep it strong.

The people themselves were doing it. That was good. The
whites and the blacks, the Catholics and Protestants and

Jews, the American-born and the foreign-born. He read that sometimes they fought with each other, and kindled new fires of bigotry. But in a national sense they were one people. Their tyrannies and intolerance were among themselves, not forced upon them by any governing power. These, then, were the people Lincoln had tried to lead "with malice toward none, with charity for all." Reading of their day-by-day struggle in the newspapers, he set his heart more firmly than ever on joining them somehow and becoming part of the great thing that was unfolding in America.

He went from the newspapers to the bookshelves, and he hunted around in the dusty piles until he found a volume that contained Lincoln's speech at Gettysburg. He stood there, studying the phrases, absorbing what they meant.

> . . . dedicated to the proposition that all men are created equal . . . new birth of freedom . . . that government of the people, by the people, for the people, shall not perish from the earth.

He thought what a glorious land Ireland would be, if she could be allowed to live by that spirit. And what a hopeful land America must be, to be working out her destiny on such principles.

He explored still more deeply into the library's shelves, and he discovered other American papers. It struck him as odd that in one old newspaper with a July 4 date he found the Declaration of Independence reprinted. He thought it strange that it should have been allowed in Australia at all, and almost incredible that it should have been allowed in a prison library. Was it indifference or ignorance that preserved it there, he wondered. No matter. It was there anyway, for him to read and study:

> . . . that all men are created equal, that they are endowed by their Creator with certain unalienable Rights, that among

these are Life, Liberty and the pursuit of Happiness. That
to secure these rights, Governments are instituted among
Men, deriving their just powers from the consent of the
governed. . . .

He thought, what a strange thing to be reading in such a
place. And what a magnificent thing to be offering to mankind! What endless horizons of hope, and what splendid justice! He spoke of it to Father Lynch one evening, when the
shadows of twilight were moving down across Fremantle and
the two of them sat in the unlighted library room and
watched the outline of Swan River going dark. There was a
little time left before he'd have to return to his cell for the
night.

"I've been reading all I could about America, Father."

The priest turned his face back from the window. "Yes,
John. I've been watching you."

"I'll get there somehow, Father. They're doing the things
I want to do—the things we'd do for Ireland, if we could.
They're trying to live like brothers—the ones who are thinking. They're saying it doesn't matter where you were born, or
where you go to pray, or what color they see in your face. If
you're an American, they say, you have a right to walk as a
free man and to help make the laws and make your home and
your family without interference from anyone. Back in Dublin I'd heard that was the way they lived in America. But here
I've learned a lot more about it—a great deal more."

Father Lynch held a match to a fresh cigar, and the light
flared briefly on the stained walls of the room. He offered a
cigar to O'Reilly. "They have their disappointments, too.
They have their sufferings and their bitterness, as all men
do."

"I'm sure of that," O'Reilly said. "But they're trying, Father. That's what counts—the trying. It may take them a
hundred years or more to get what they want, but they know

what it is. They'll reach it someday. A nation of tolerance and brotherhood. A place where men can work together and be friends, and still kneel at different altars and vote for different leaders. I want to be part of that, Father."

"So I gathered from your Fenian friends. They think that by being a good American you can help Ireland." The priest was quiet a moment. "I think so, too."

"I shouldn't ask, I suppose, but can you help me get there?"

Father Lynch shrugged. "I expected you to ask. I've been thinking about it some. I don't know. It's a hard thing to answer."

The wall clock ticked away slowly, and O'Reilly waited for him to go on.

"You'll be going down the coast tomorrow," the priest said. "Down to Bunbury, and then into the Bush."

O'Reilly was startled, but he kept silent. He hadn't expected to be moved so soon, though there was no reason not to expect it.

Father Lynch might have been reading his thoughts. "I've had you with me four weeks, John," he said. "That's longer than I'd hoped for. Now they'll be moving you along again. I saw your orders this afternoon."

"Orders? What did they say?"

"You'll get them in the morning. They tell you what time the boat sails, and they direct you to deliver three articles on board and in good condition. The articles are listed on a bill of lading—one bag, one hammock, one convict No. 9843. That's you."

O'Reilly grimaced. "They might have listed me first. That's the least they could have done."

The priest laughed shortly, and drew on his cigar. "Are you ready to go, John?"

"Not really, and yet, yes. I've enjoyed it here with you. The first real pleasure and companionship I've had in two years. I want to move along, though. There are bound to be just so many steps between today's chains and tomorrow's freedom. I want to put them behind me."

"Are you ready inside yourself?"

"You heard my confession. I'm ready."

"It won't be easy. You may die—as many others have done."

"I don't think I will."

The priest was silent for several moments. Then he said, "It's time to go back to your cell now, John. You'll be away at dawn, and probably I'll never see you again. Keep your eyes where they are now, John—on the high peaks, on the stars, on the tall, bright places where all men stand equal with a hand in God's. If you get to America, stay there and help them on the path they're climbing—for the higher they go, the better for Ireland and the other suffering lands.

"Now, just one thing more. One day, down there in the forests, another priest will come and visit you. That'll be Patrick McCabe—Father Mac, the convicts call him. His 'parish,' if you can use that word, is several hundred miles of wild Bush country, and he stops at all the campfires. I'll see that he'll know all about you when he gets there. Listen to him, and trust him. He's the only man in all Australia who can get you out of this."

Father Lynch got to his feet. He gave O'Reilly a quick, affectionate embrace on the shoulders. "You'll have to be going to your cell, John. God bless you—and God be with you. And please have faith and patience. No matter how many months you have to wait, don't try to escape on your own. It may take a long time, but Father Mac will show up someday. Don't try anything until he comes."

14. THE MAHOGANY FOREST

HE WOULD WAIT for Father Mac—wait and be patient in a region that seemed timeless, and where the dragging hours from one sunrise to the next were without a beginning or an end.

It was only an eighty-mile coastal voyage from Fremantle to Bunbury, on the shore of Geographe Bay, but it was far enough to take him into a new world that was startling in its primitive crudeness. From Bunbury they moved him, by horse and by foot, deeper and deeper into a raw wilderness that seemed, all at once, majestic and fantastic and frightening. When he reached the end of his trail, he was in a part of Western Australia that most men avoided as they would a region of hell. Men went there in irons, to cut the huge mahogany trees that rose from the noisome swamps and to work in the road gangs that fought desperately to break a clear path through the dense jungle. But rarely did any men go there of their own choice; rather, they went only when driven by a whip or a club or a gun.

O'Reilly found himself in a region where time had come to a halt. It was as though all the rest of the world had moved on, a million years ago, and had left this land behind. His journey ended at a convict camp inside the Koagulup Swamp. It was a dark and dismal tangled lake, with black waters that seemed to have no limit of depth and with tremendous dark caverns of vines and vegetation where the sunlight had not penetrated since the world was young.

Beyond stretched the region called the Vasse, reaching far off through the forests to where the mountains began. It was a place of trackless solitude, where the native Bushmen moved about unclothed. It was a place, too, of hidden, mysterious riches, where the Bush tribal chiefs wore thick armlets and breastplates of pure hammered gold, and yet through years of cutting and blasting and digging on the jungle roads, no white man had ever found an ounce of the metal.

The men around O'Reilly were the lowest dregs of England's criminal pools. They had been sent into the forests with no hope of ever getting out again. They had been sent in to hack at the jungled mass until they died, and if they pushed the great Vasse road only one mile deeper into the interior it was enough, for when a man died there was always another on the way down from Fremantle to replace him. For those men, it was a life of endless toil and sweat, of the shrill yells of the guards, of whisperings among themselves, of floggings and of loneliness.

There was a bond among the men, but it was a bond of common despair and not of friendship. O'Reilly was used to that feeling. He'd known it before, in other prison gangs. It neither disturbed nor discouraged him when he met it again, at the end of his journey from Fremantle and Bunbury. His was a lonely life, too, and had been for many months.

They put him in one of the slab-hut road camps, where the swamp forest loomed tall by day and the open fires burned by night, and the wet, decaying tree stumps glowed with phosphorus in the moonlight. As a poet, the region gripped him and held him fascinated. It was weirdly beautiful with its monstrous vegetation and its gigantic trees. It was frightening and stifling with its density and its darkness. It was like the land of a strange dream, containing animals and birds that had long ago disappeared from all other parts of the world but that still lived on here, as though in some lost and forgotten primeval age. As a convict, he suffered and toiled beside the rest of the gang—with a shovel and pick, where the dirt and mud and rocks had to be leveled; with an ax, where the giant trees of a lost age had to be felled and destroyed.

The hardest hours to endure came in the baking midsummer days of February. Then the heat grew so intense and so heavy that all the Bush, for miles up through the Vasse, lay stifled and without motion. On days like that, with the sun at its most scorching arc, Boyle O'Reilly would pause in his labor and look around in wonder at the complete stillness of the country. He would feel the heat burning into his naked back and the sweat crawling down his face and his bare stomach, and he would stare around as far as his eyes could see, and it was always the same. Complete stillness. It fascinated him, and he longed for a chance to write about the weird sensations it gave a man—perhaps to tell about it in a poem.

He'd look around at the big mahogany trees and the gum trees, and the matted vines and tangled thorns, and it would be as though they were painted against a blue-copper sky. Nothing moved. He'd look across the tops of the flat banksia trees and see the heads of thousands of white cockatoos, but never a head that moved. The birds would sit there as motionless as though made of white stone.

On the ground around him he'd see the armies of traveling ants, resting beneath low underbrush, or a snake or an iguana, without motion. And over it all the sun beat down its scorching fire with a heat so fierce and deadening that no parrot screamed in the trees and no insect made a sound in the grass.

Then there'd come a harsh cry from the gang foreman: "O'Reilly! Back to work!"

He'd start, surprised, and quickly move into line with the

others and swing his ax and breathe in hot gasps and feel
the sweat run down his forehead and blind him. And far off
in the Bush, on either side of him, he'd hear the ring of another ax, and another, and the shouts of the prison foremen.
All nature could rest on those terribly hot days, but not the
convicts. From dawn to twilight they worked, whatever the
sun might do in the sky.

It was one month after he had joined the road gang in the
forests when he was called out of line at midday by the shout
of a guard sitting on a nearby knoll. He had been working
with two other convicts, both serving life for murder. One
of them—a Tom Kelly from Belfast—had grown old in the
Bush, and now was a tired, sick man. Working with him
meant doing the work of two men, for Kelly was feeble—
willing and earnest, but feeble. The Bush had long since
taken its toll of him.

They worked now, the three of them, naked to the heat,
trying to bring down a huge mahogany tree at the edge of a
swampy pool. It was impossible to get a good footing, to get
the leverage for a clean swing of the ax. Thorny vines had
torn their arms and their shoulders. Dirt and sweat had made
them half-blind. Still the tree was almost ready to fall when
the shout came from the guard.

O'Reilly hesitated just a moment, without turning his
head. Then he went on with his work. Beside him, Kelly
muttered a warning.

"He's callin', O'Reilly. Ye'd best go."

O'Reilly kept swinging his ax. He spoke under his breath.
"Can't hear him. We can get this down in a few more minutes. Just the two of you—you'd need all day, and maybe get
flogged. Let him wait."

The guard shouted again. "O'Reilly! Get over here!"

He went on swinging his ax without a break. The other

two worked with mallet and wedge. The tree began to creak.

A third yell came from the guard and a violent curse as he climbed to his feet and started moving angrily across the hot sunlit clearing toward O'Reilly.

The tree creaked again, and began to strain. One more pounding swing—and there it was! It toppled slowly at first, picking up speed, and finally crashed to earth like a stricken giant. The three men stood back and wiped their faces. The convict Kelly spoke quickly.

"Thanks, mate. That helped a lot. Watch it, now—here 'e comes."

"O'Reilly!" The guard stormed up and grabbed him by the shoulder and spun him around so that he almost fell. "We'll 'ave discipline, or ye'll get th' whip! Don't make out ye couldn't 'ear me."

"Sorry, sir. I wasn't paying attention. It was a hard tree to bring down."

The guard stared at him closely, unconvinced. "Anyways, if ye're late it's no fault of mine. Ye'll catch it on th' other end. Orders just came," he said. "Put on some clothes and get back down the road to th' station office. They've a new job to put you on. Shake it up now!"

O'Reilly picked up his shirt and trousers and turned to leave. As he moved away, he caught a glance of thanks from Kelly and his mate. He smiled wryly inside. Just with a few extra ax blows he'd saved them several hours of work and made the guard leave his seat in the shade and walk through the scorching sunlight. It was reward enough for a few minutes of work. He set off down the rough cleared road, wondering what the new assignment would be.

It was a hot and tiring journey, close to two miles, with the sun beating down almost every yard of the way. He tried to walk close to the edge of the road and stay in the shade, but the footing was dangerous there. He gave it up, after stumbling a few times, and he stayed in the middle of the path.

Along the way he found himself wondering about Father Mac, and about how long it would be before the priest's wanderings brought him to this convict outpost. It might be many weeks. Perhaps it would be better to try an escape while waiting. But no—not yet. The Bush mass along the roadside was as thick and impenetrable as a stone wall. He never could make it alone that way. If he went twenty feet in from the road, he'd be lost. They wouldn't even have to hunt for him. They could just wait for him to stumble out onto the road again at some other point, or wait for him to die in the jungle. And if they did hunt for him, and went after him with natives, they'd catch him almost at once. Then he'd get the floggings, the beatings, the hunger and thirst, and all the other punishments of the convict camp. No, it would be better to wait for Father Mac—wait and plan—wait and pray.

He reached the station office, hot and exhausted. He tried hopelessly to wipe some of the dirt from his face and hands. He gave it up. They'd sent for him, so they'd get him dirt and all. It wasn't his fault if he couldn't keep clean.

He went up the rough steps of the main slab building and walked inside. An overseer sitting behind the desk looked up and appraised him indifferently. O'Reilly didn't know who he was. The officers and guards were changed so often, it was hard to keep track of them. And anyhow, all of them seemed to live in another world that looked down upon convicts as a troublesome type of animal, part savage and part stupid. There was little point in trying to remember identities on that basis.

"You sent for me, sir." O'Reilly broke the silence. "I'm O'Reilly—outer Vasse station."

The overseer stared at him coldly. "You don't need to tell

me what I did, prisoner. I'm not a fool. Remember I did the
sending and you did the coming."

"Yes, sir."

The overseer looked through a group of papers on his desk
and placed one of them on top of the pile and appeared to be
studying it.

"It says here you have a good record. You work hard, never
break the rules, and you're dependable."

O'Reilly remained silent, knowing he'd be rebuked if he
said anything.

After a moment the overseer spoke again. "It says you're a
good influence on the other prisoners—that there's no trouble when you're around—they like you and work well with
you.

"With all that on your record," the overseer went on, "I'm
damned if I know why they want to give you a change of job.
I'd say leave you where you're doing some good. But then, I
have to take orders, same as you." He glanced up at O'Reilly,
and then down again. "This order says you're to work out of
this office as a convict constable. You know what that is?"

"Yes, sir."

"Well, in case you don't I'm supposed to tell you anyhow.
That's the rules. You'll wear a red stripe on your sleeve—
that's your badge. You'll gain a few privileges—a clock, pen
and paper, a hut of your own. Some days you'll be an aide to
the foreman of a work party—a road gang, maybe, or whatever's doing that day. Help him keep order, and see that the
work's done right. If there's any trouble with the convicts,
you help put it down—help keep them in line. Think you
can do that?"

"Yes, sir." It sounded good. He could help the convicts a
lot—make their jobs easier—maybe give them a little rest
here and there.

"Also," the overseer went on, "you'll work as a courier. You'll carry messages from station to station, and when there's a mutineer to take back to prison, you'll go along to see that he gets there. And God help you, O'Reilly, if he breaks away."

"Yes, sir."

"Now, then, prisoner, you're to start work tomorrow morning. So get back to your camp and report out. Then hurry back here and I'll have a place assigned to you. Obey that order promptly, O'Reilly, and all the other orders you'll get. You didn't obey promptly when I sent for you. By my estimate, you were six minutes late in getting here. Something must have detained you."

Six minutes late in a world that was timeless! O'Reilly fought down an expression of contempt for the overseer. Six minutes was just about the length of time it had taken to help Kelly and the other convict bring down the big tree and to stop twice briefly along the road to recover from the heat of the sun.

"O'Reilly!"

"Yes, sir."

"You'll find we're very strict with our constables. They're chosen men, so we have to insist they obey promptly and thoroughly. Otherwise, the punishments are severe. Setting an example to the prisoners, you know."

"I understand." O'Reilly nodded.

"You may go now. And hurry back."

O'Reilly turned quickly and started for the door. He felt pleased with the prospects of the new work. He pulled the screen door open and stepped outside. The overseer's voice brought him to a quick halt.

"O'Reilly! Come back here!"

What now? He turned and hurried back inside, and stood at the desk again.

The overseer favored him with a humorless smile. "I almost forgot, prisoner. Some mail came up from Fremantle a couple of days ago. There's a letter here for you. We've read it, to see if it's all right." He leaned across the desk and held out an opened envelope with a heavy black border.

O'Reilly felt his heart wrench. Father Lynch's words flashed through his mind. His mother! It could only be that! —news from home, and news of her death. He reached for it, and his hand suddenly was shaking.

The overseer snatched it back just as it touched his fingers. He held it loosely a moment, smiling at O'Reilly with a look of cold malice.

"I told you the rules for constables are strict," he said. "You were six minutes late reporting here. You'll get this letter six months from today."

He tossed it into his desk drawer.

"That's all, prisoner. Go back and report out."

Six months later, to the exact day, O'Reilly read the letter. His mother had died at Dowth Castle.

15. FATHER MAC

FATHER MAC was coming.

The news made its way somehow from camp to camp and hut to hut, and out to the convict gangs at the far edge of the swamp: Father Mac was coming to the Vasse. O'Reilly heard about it, without quite knowing where or how. It was always that way, when the convicts passed the word on important news.

By that time his work as a convict constable had settled into a pattern. On certain days he walked from camp to camp and station to station, delivering messages and gathering reports on stores and conditions. For the long trips, where the camps lay many miles apart, they let him use a horse. For the short trips, he had to make his own way as well as he could, and still be on time. When all the reports were collected, at the end of the circuit, he would carry them to the base station at Bunbury and pick up the mail and messages from Fremantle. He would distribute these along the trails and the convict roads on his way back. Then, after the completion of each circuit, he would be assigned for a few days to some work-gang foreman. On those days he could sometimes find a reason for directing the foreman's attention to some matter back at the station, so that the prisoners could get a chance to sit down and rest. It was risky, he knew, but it was helping to make their lives a little easier. There wasn't anything else they could look forward to.

He had managed to get the foreman away and was sitting with a group at a campfire one evening when Father Mac appeared. They heard his horse first, coming down the road in the darkness, and they cut off their conversation abruptly and broke up the circle around the fire. When Father Mac rode into the glow of the firelight he saw O'Reilly sitting alone with a limp whip in his hands, while the prisoners lay scattered on the ground in their blankets, apparently asleep.

The priest dismounted and walked across the clearing and held out his hand with a smile. "It's a good act, John O'Reilly," he said quietly, "but you won't be needing it with me. I'd be letting them sit around and talk, too, if I were the constable. As it is, I'm only Father Mac."

O'Reilly liked the man on sight. He was slim and clear-eyed, about O'Reilly's height but older. His hair was black. His face was bronzed with the sun and lined with the rigors of fifteen years spent traveling up and down the Bush, moving among the worst criminals England could get together.

"It does them good to talk," O'Reilly said. "I'll get them up again, so they can spend some minutes with you."

The priest put a warning hand on his arm. "Some other time, John. Some other time, but not now. I'll see them later. Your foreman's coming down the road anyhow. That's one reason I rode on ahead—because I've heard you take chances like this with the prisoners. The convicts respect you for it, John."

"I'd been hoping you'd come soon," O'Reilly said. He was eager to get alone with the man and talk.

The priest shrugged helplessly. "I was late. It takes a long time to get around. Hundreds of miles to cover, and hundreds of lost and hopeless men. And I've nobody to help me. I came when I could—and that's tonight."

"Then you've seen Father Lynch?"

He nodded. "Many weeks ago. But John, we can't talk here. I've told your foreman I need you tonight—to help me with some reports. He's letting me keep you as long as I want. We can talk after he gets here, and when we can get away. He'll be only a few minutes now."

And so they went off and spent the next few hours beside a clear lake that lay in the woods at a safe distance from the camp. They built a small fire there, and watched the reflection of its flames on the water, and they shared meat and old wine that Father Mac had brought along in his grubsack. And after the food and drink were gone, they had a cigar apiece that Father Lynch had sent. The tobacco was dry after so long a time, but the smoke was welcome.

O'Reilly told him his plans. "I've been getting ready for months, Father. Probably Father Lynch told you—somehow, I'm going to America. That's where they're doing the work I want to do. Perhaps that way I can help Ireland, too. I think I'd make a good American."

The priest nodded, and shifted his cigar. "I think you would, too. But it's a wild dream, John—a wild dream, that's all. Better forget it—right away."

O'Reilly shook his head. "No, it's more than a dream. It's a necessary part of my life. And I've planned it with that in mind. I've had months now to get ready. I've put away the things I'll need—stolen them and hidden them. A knife, a rope, a pair of civilian shoes—so they can't trace the convict's footmark—a package of matches, a bottle of fever pills. I've got things like that all hidden away, Father. I'm going to escape somehow. But I've waited to see you, because Father Lynch said you're the only man in Australia who can help me get away. Will you help me, Father?"

"You've picked an excellent way to commit suicide," the priest replied. "That's the best I can say for your dream."

To O'Reilly, it was like a slap in the face.

"Where would you go and how would you get there?" Father Mac went on. "Without help, without somebody to guide you, you'd get lost and die in the Bush."

"Then get somebody to guide me, Father."

"Without a shelter, somewhere to flee to and hide in, the guards would be sure to catch up with you."

"You must know a man with a shelter, Father, after fifteen years in this country."

The priest drew on his cigar. "Then, too, which way would you go? You couldn't escape across land even if you stayed alive, for all the police in Australia would be watching for you. Sooner or later you'd have to show up somewhere. And they're patient, John, they're patient. They'd still be looking for you after twenty years. And how about the other way? How could you escape across an ocean or two, when you haven't even a boat to sail across this lake? You've nowhere to go, John. And no way to get there. I'm sorry. The best thing to do is to forget it."

"I can't give it up that easily," O'Reilly said. "I can't toss it away like that."

"Neither could I." Father Mac sighed. "But it's hopeless. It's been on my mind for many weeks now, and I've tried and tried to think of a way to help you. I still say it's suicide. Don't be thinking of it any more, John. Please forget the whole thing. It's better that way."

O'Reilly took a long pull at his cigar and said nothing for several minutes. He listened to the night noises, while he collected his thoughts. A fish leaped and splashed far out on the lake, and it reminded him of the times he'd heard the salmon and the trout leaping in the cold, clear waters of Ireland. Somewhere in the underbrush behind him he heard the sound of a small animal moving about, sniffing the ground, and he remembered the little fat brown spaniel he'd owned when he'd been a boy at play along the River Boyne.

He drew his breath for a long talk. "Father," he said, "you love Ireland, don't you?"

"No man loves her more, John."

"Then, Father, listen to some stories I'm going to tell you. Listen and remember—remember the slope of Tara, and the fishermen of Galway, and the fog that comes in sweet and salt over Dublin. Remember Croagh Patrick and the Western Sea—the little children dancing at the crossroads. Remember the soft, sad songs, so old that nobody knew a thousand years ago who'd written them, and so beautiful they'll still be rare another thousand years from now. Remember the good things of Ireland, Father, while I talk. And remember, too, the things that are sorrowful—the mothers who die without knowing what's happened to their sons; the priests who've been hanged for saying Mass; the terrible sound of the stranger's boot at your door in the night, and the shout that orders you out while he burns down your cottage.

"And now listen, Father. There are things I've got to tell you. They're the reasons why I must escape, and why you must help me. I want you to listen now. Just listen to what I have to say."

He talked for two long hours, while the half-moon rose over the tops of the mahogany forest and the light of the planets wheeled in the sky, and the night noises of the Bush were all around them. He talked of prisons and dreams, of poetry and death. He talked of what man was doing to man, and of how he hoped to help change those things; how he wanted only to get to America and be an American, and to tell the listeners that brotherhood is better than hate, justice better than prejudice, tolerance more lasting than tyranny. And he told how he hoped that someday some part of that message might cross the sea from America to other lands, and in turn help Ireland to be the fair land it should always have

been. He talked until he felt exhausted, worn by his own intensity, and yet wanting to go on talking for hours to come.
He poured out his heart and his desperation.

And when he fell silent at last, he waited for a long time
while Father Mac said nothing. The priest sat deep in
thought, with his hands clasped over his knees. Then at
length he got to his feet and held out his hand for O'Reilly
to stand up beside him.

He put a hand on O'Reilly's shoulder. "You shouldn't be
here," he said. "You should be where you want to be—in
America. Let me think out a plan for getting you there. I'll
find the way. Believe in me, and however long it takes, wait
until I send word to you. You'll do that? Good! I promise I'll
find a way.

"And now, would you like me to hear your confession? It
must have been a long time you've waited. A terribly long
time."

O'Reilly awoke at dawn the next day and went to join the
foreman with the road gang, and he learned that Father Mac
already had gone on his way. The convicts were in a quiet,
comforted mood from having been with the priest and listened to him and talked with him in the hours before sunrise.
He must have had no sleep at all, O'Reilly thought. And how
long now before there'd be some word? How long before he'd
hear?

Almost another six months of weary waiting went by before the message came. When it did come, it came in an un-
expected, startling way.

It happened one afternoon, when he had collected the last
of the station reports at the end of the circuit, and while he
was walking down the long Vasse road on the tiring hike to
Bunbury depot. The nearest station camp lay miles behind

him, and the straight road was deserted in both directions. As he had done so many times before, Boyle O'Reilly felt as though he were the only man alive in all the land. There was nobody else to be seen or heard.

The trees gradually fell away on either side of the road, and then the underbrush grew thin, and he knew he was coming to a big plain called the Race Course. He'd heard talk, from time to time in the past, that the government someday intended to clear the plain of its shrubs and bushes and try to develop it, one way or another. He wondered idly why it should matter to anyone.

He wasn't surprised, therefore, when he came abreast of the center of the plain and saw a lone tall man off in the distance swinging an ax at the undergrowth. O'Reilly glanced at him absently, across the distance, and then turned his face to the road again and kept plodding along toward Bunbury.

Then, abruptly, he pulled up short. From across the plain, where the man had been working, a loud shrill "Coo-ee!" caught his hearing. O'Reilly turned and stared back and saw that the man was striding over the field toward him with his ax slung over his shoulder. He wondered what the stranger could possibly want. Working for the Government, he ought to know better than to be seen talking with anyone in a convict's garb.

O'Reilly waited, curious. The man's long strides brought him quickly across the plain to the edge of the road, and he stepped out then with a broad grin on his face. He was red-haired and rugged, with fists the size of mallets.

"Frightened you, eh? I'm sorry." The stranger came to a halt by O'Reilly's side and glanced carelessly up and down the road.

O'Reilly felt strangely uneasy. This could be a trap, to see if he'd break the rules and to punish him if he did. Worse yet—and the thought was a frightening one—it could be a trap that had something to do with his plan for escape. He didn't know how that could have happened, but he'd have to be careful. He'd have to wait, and make sure.

The big stranger held out his hand. "My name's Maguire. I'm a friend of Father Mac's. He told me I'd see you pass this way."

O'Reilly shook hands uncertainly, convinced that the man was out to trick him.

"You're O'Reilly, aren't you? Boyle O'Reilly? You look like Father Mac said you would."

"Yes, I'm O'Reilly."

The man's grin broadened. "Well, then, that's all I want to know. Father Mac told me to stay here on the Race Course till someday you'd go by, and then to give you a message from him."

O'Reilly frowned. "Aren't you a government man? Working here like this, you must be."

Maguire chuckled. "Sure I am—for convenience—till you come along and get this message. Then, after the plan works out, I'll quit the bloody place and get back to my farm. I only took the job 'cause Father Mac asked me to. How else could he get word to you anyhow?" Maguire was beginning to sound impatient.

"Word?" O'Reilly shrugged. "Word about what? What's he want to know?"

Maguire fixed him with a long, cool stare. "Well," he said at last, "I guess you're right, at that. You can't just go along trusting a stranger that calls out as you walk by—not and keep your head on your neck, you can't. Here, O'Reilly, read this. Then listen to me."

He pulled a wallet from his dusty trousers, and took out a small card and handed it to O'Reilly.

O'Reilly recognized the priest's handwriting. He'd seen it on several papers that night when Father Mac had opened his grubsack and taken out meat and wine. The message was simple. All it said was: "Trust Maguire and believe what he tells you. It's a plan that may work. (Signed) Father Mac."

O'Reilly felt his heart jump with eagerness. Maguire was grinning again. The big man looked up and down the road once more, making sure it was deserted, and then he told the story briefly.

"Come February—that's only two months, isn't it—come February there'll be two American whaling barks putting in at Bunbury for water. They're the *Vigilant* and the *Gazelle* —both out of New Bedford.

"Father Mac says he's going to get you on one of these ships or we'll all lose our necks trying. My neck, too, O'Reilly— and it's a neck I'm fond of. He's got a good plan that you'll hear about later.

"That's all there is to tell you right now. Don't do anything yourself. Just wait till you hear again—either from me or Father Mac. Then do what you're told, and do it fast.

"That's all for now, O'Reilly." He slapped him on the shoulder. "You'll be a free man in February, sure as my name is Maguire!"

He turned and strode away, leaving O'Reilly standing dazed in the middle of the road. He turned just once more, part way across the field.

"One other thing, O'Reilly!" he shouted back. "He says God bless you!—and be a good American!"

III

FLIGHT

(February 1869—November 1869)

He teaches the secret of manhood—the watchword of
  those who aspire—
That man must follow freedom, though it lead through
  blood and fire . . .

From "The Patriot's Grave."

16. ESCAPE TO SEA

THE NEXT FEW WEEKS, O'Reilly felt, were the slowest of his life. But they passed and the scorching heat of Australia's midsummer was back in the Vasse again. It was February now. And as he walked along the road again, returning from Bunbury with station orders, he thought back over the year that had gone by—a full year of labor in the Bush, a year of monotony and toil and sweat, and a full year of hoping and dreaming of escape. Now he was ready to try it; all he needed was the signal.

The brush fell away on either side of the Vasse road as he approached the Race Course. He'd passed it several times since the day he'd met Maguire there. Twice he'd seen Maguire at work, cutting wood on the far side of the field, but the big man had given him no sign of recognition, and he'd walked by without stopping, and wondered if the plans were going all right.

Now again he came to the plain. And again he saw Maguire swinging an ax at a clump of shrubs close to the side of the road.

The big man stopped and wiped his face and grinned as O'Reilly came abreast. He stepped out to the road. He braced himself on his ax handle, and glanced quickly up and down in both directions.

"Good to be seeing you, O'Reilly. You ready to leave?"

O'Reilly suddenly felt as though he had been carrying a great weight and at last had found a place to put it down. His heart began to pound. He grinned back at Maguire.

"You mean it, Maguire? I've been ready for a year!"

"It's not going to be easy."

"Easy? You think it's easy living like this? Living like a slave? Seeing men tortured and worked to death?" His voice began to rise.

Maguire put a hand on his arm, to calm him down.

"Of course not," he said earnestly. "It must be like living in hell. No man should have to stand it. But this other thing —if you fail, and they get you back, you know what's going to happen."

"I know." O'Reilly nodded quickly. "They'll break me. They'll try to kill me. But it's worth the risk. Better take a chance on death than stay half-alive."

"Listen, then," Maguire said. "Sit down here, and we'll go over the plans."

They moved off the road, and sat on a hummock of thick, dry grass. O'Reilly felt the heat of the sun blazing down on his back, and he heard the drowsy singing of the midsummer insects on the plain, and he wondered hopefully if the time had really arrived when he could count on making a try for it —putting this land behind him and making a break for freedom. Maguire spoke in low tones, keeping his eyes on O'Reilly's face, holding his attention fixed.

"The whaling barks came into Bunbury yesterday," he said. "The *Vigilant,* with Captain Baker. The *Gazelle,* with Captain Gifford. The *Vigilant* will sail first—probably two days from now. Father Mac has fixed it up with Captain Baker to pick you up from a boat in Geographe Bay. We'll have the boat waiting for you below Bunbury, and I'll take you there myself. Then we'll have to row out and intercept the bark. And pray to God we can make it! But if we don't make it, Captain Baker says he may cruise around for two or three days on the lookout for you.

"Now, then, you're to leave your hut tonight, sharp at eight o'clock. Go into the Bush to the place where you talked with Father Mac—the place beside the lake. You know the trail that leads from there to the Vasse road? Sure about that now? Take that path and follow it all the way to the edge of the road. Don't move from that spot. Lie there in the grass. I'll be riding my horse on the road for some time before that, up nearer the camp, to make sure there're no guards around. If it's all clear, I'll be coming down the road about the time you'll be hiding in the grass. If there's anybody nearby, or if they're on to you by that time, I'll just ride by quiet-like. But if you hear me whistle the first bars of 'Patrick's Day,' then come running out, and we'll make a break for it. There'll be another horse waiting for you, and I'll probably have a friend with me, a man named Mallory. That's all now, until to-night."

Maguire clapped him on the shoulder, got to his feet, and started off across the plain, swinging his ax as he went. O'Reilly moved out on the road again, and walked on toward the camp. He felt dizzy with nervous excitement. He looked at his hands, and saw they were trembling. After so many months, so many prisons and cells and whips and chains! The thought that he might be miles away by the next morning left him weak. He slowed his walk, trying to get control of his nerves before reaching the camp. After a while he saw that his hands no longer trembled and he felt that his head was clear again, and he smiled to himself. Somehow, it seemed impossible that he would fail now.

After supper that evening, alone in his hut, he collected the things he had hidden in the months gone by—the knife, the matches, the fever pills. He made them into a small package, and put it inside his shirt. He glanced out the open door to look for the guards. The camp was quiet. The shadows

were growing dark across the clearing. A small fire smoked
and flared. The stars were beginning to brighten overhead.

He turned back into the hut and struck a match to a candle. Then he took the pen and paper that he used in his work
as a constable, and he wrote a long letter to his father in
Drogheda. He told his father what his plans were—what he
was about to try—how he hoped somehow to get to the
United States, and to do the kind of work that might help
Ireland and might, in some way, help men to understand
each other better. And he wrote, too, of the possibility that
his father might never see the letter, but that if it arrived
in Drogheda, it would mean that the escape had been successful and the letter had been mailed from the first port the
whaling bark had entered. He asked his father to give the
letter to the Dublin newspapers some time in May, for by
that time he expected to be far beyond the reach of prison
officers. And perhaps, if the letter were printed, it might give
hope and courage to other men who were fighting against
despotism.

"God bless you, Father," he finished, "and please say a
prayer for me at Mother's grave."

He sealed the envelope, addressed it, and put it inside his
shirt. He wondered, wistfully, if it ever would reach Ireland.

As he finished, he heard footsteps outside approaching the
hut. It was the camp warden, making his nightly rounds, his
nightly seven-o'clock check on the prisoners. O'Reilly quickly
busied himself with the papers he had brought from Bunbury
that day. He was leaning over them at his table, with his pen
in his hand, when the warden opened the door and looked
in and stared at him in silence for several moments. O'Reilly
glanced up, questioningly.

The warden nodded at the papers and scowled. "Camp reports, I suppose."

"Yes, sir."

"Get on with it, then." He turned away from the door and went back into the shadows outside, checking on the huts one by one.

As soon as he had gone, O'Reilly took off his convict boots with the telltale marks on the soles. He changed to the civilian boots he had hidden away months before. Then he blew out his candle and sat quietly in the darkness, listening to the tick of the clock. It seemed that never before in his life had the minutes been so long.

One hour later he slipped silently through the doorway, moved into the shadows at the edge of the clearing, and disappeared into the darkness of the swamp.

He made his way swiftly but stealthily through the Bush, heading for the lake where he had sat with Father Mac. He looked up at the bright stars overhead, and thanked God for making it a perfect night for an escape—bright above and dark on the ground. He quickened his step, eager to get through the woods and be on his way.

Then abruptly he halted. Somebody was following him, close behind! He heard the sound of a dry branch snapping underfoot. He swung around on the trail, straining his eyes to see through the darkness. His brain throbbed and his anger rose. To be cheated at this point! He clenched his fists and waited. He decided to fight his way out if he had to.

Then he heard a low whistle, and a figure moved from the shadows beside the trail.

A hoarse whisper, "O'Reilly! It's me—Tom Kelly!"

Kelly stepped quickly to his side and held up his hand for silence. "Don't talk, O'Reilly. You're safe. I saw you leave. I'll help you."

Help him? What could Kelly do but hinder him, he thought bitterly.

Kelly whispered again. "Tell me where you're heading. When the alarm goes out, I'll steer them off on the wrong scent. Geographe Bay, is it? Good! I'll get them started in the other direction. Good-by, O'Reilly. God speed!"

The convict grabbed O'Reilly's hand in a quick, strong grip, and without another word vanished swiftly down the trail toward the camp. O'Reilly turned and hurried off again through the woods. He reached the lake, and stepped into the dark trail that led away to the Vasse road. He had a long way to go, and the pursuit might start at any moment.

It was three hours later, when the shadows finally thinned along the edge of the trail, and he could see the stars again through the branches overhead, that suddenly the path ended and the road lay before him. He lay down in the grass, beneath a big gum tree, watching the silent, deserted roadway and praying that Maguire would come soon.

The minutes dragged by. It must have been half an hour. Then faintly, in the distance, he heard the sound of horses coming at a fast gallop. He tensed, afraid that it might be a mounted patrol, or a search party from the camp. The horses came closer—closer—and then their gallop slowed to a walk, and they snorted to an abrupt halt close to the end of the trail.

For a moment the night was still. Then, softly but clearly, O'Reilly heard the whistled notes of "Patrick's Day." He jumped to his feet and ran into the road. Maguire and another man were there, with a spare horse saddled and ready.

He heard Maguire give a low, glad cry.

"You made it! O'Reilly, meet Mallory! Quick! We've no time to waste."

O'Reilly swung into the empty saddle. Without another word the three men wheeled their horses about and set off at a swift gallop down the road.

They traveled for hours in silence, urging their horses to the limits of their speed. O'Reilly never knew what course they followed. Maguire, riding out in front, led them on a fast route, from road to trail, from trail to plain, through woods and fields and sandy clearings. O'Reilly marveled at the man's sense of direction, for he never hesitated at a turn and never slackened speed. They galloped on and on through the darkness, and the only sound in the night was the drumming sound of the hoofbeats.

It was still dark, although daybreak was near, when Maguire suddenly reined in his horse at the edge of a sandy field. He dismounted, and motioned to O'Reilly and Mallory to do the same. Then Maguire whistled once and gestured to the other two to stay quiet. After a moment they heard an answering whistle from nearby and off to the left.

Three men hurried into view. Without a word one of them mounted Maguire's horse, grabbed the reins of the other two, and galloped away. Maguire started off across the field at a fast walk, keeping the others in Indian file behind him— Mallory, then O'Reilly, then the two newcomers bringing up the rear. O'Reilly glanced back at them once, and saw they were covering up the footprints as they went, trailing a light rig of shrub branches. They walked on for an hour, and finally stopped at the bed of a dry swamp that lay beside the sea. Close by, a broad creek angled down across the marshland. And there, in the matted grass, Maguire and Mallory knelt and pulled away the coverings that concealed a dory.

O'Reilly had no idea where he was, except that he was somewhere on the shore of Geographe Bay, and that out there on the water he had a rendezvous with an American whaling bark. That much he knew, and he knew, too, that many miles now lay between him and the prison camp, but that search

parties probably already were hunting for his trail. He hoped
Tom Kelly would be able to lead them far astray.

The bark *Vigilant* sailed from Australia without taking
O'Reilly aboard. Twice the contact was nearly made, and
twice it failed. On the first try Maguire and the two strangers
from the sandy field—his cousins—rowed O'Reilly far out
across Geographe Bay, on a course that they felt would intercept the *Vigilant* when she sailed from Bunbury. They pulled
mile after mile through the heavy seas, with the sun blazing
fiercely on their naked waists and with giant sharks from time
to time nosing their boat and turning lazily under their oars.

Far out at sea, with the shore only a dim line on the horizon, they rested on their oars. O'Reilly's heart was light, for
he could see the whaler rounding a distant headland and
coming their way with all sails spread.

She was a beautiful sight, with the sunlight shining on her
white canvas and with the sea foaming beneath her bow.
Closer and closer she came, heading straight for the little boat
and swiftly eating the distance that lay between. But she
never came about. Whether it was the reflection of the sunlight on the water, or the smallness of their craft, or what the
cause, O'Reilly never knew. He only knew that the *Vigilant*
went foaming by less than two miles distant, and that all
their shouts and the waving of shirts on oars never caught the
attention of any man on deck or in the rigging. As they
watched in despair, the *Vigilant* headed straight out to sea.
They stared after her until she was hull down on the Indian
Ocean, and still going away.

And so they turned back to shore, dejected and bitter,
faced now with the problem of hiding O'Reilly somewhere
until another contact could be arranged. They left him alone
that evening in the shelter of a little sandy valley, and he
watched them hurry away, knowing that now his chances of

making an escape were slim and doubtful. Maguire and Mallory would have to ride to Bunbury, and perhaps waste days trying to arrange for him to be taken aboard another whaler. And meanwhile dozens of search parties would be out on the hunt for him, from Bunbury all the way to the Vasse, using horses and trained dogs and skilled native trackers who knew every trail and hideaway in the countryside. He fell asleep under the stars that night feeling lonely and dejected, and with his hand on the letter he had so hopefully written to his father.

He was awake before sunrise, straining his ears to catch the sounds of any search party that might be in the area. There was nothing to hear—only the occasional scream of a parrot and the rustling of the breeze on the beach grass and the pounding of the heavy surf along the shore. He remembered that Captain Baker had said he might keep the *Vigilant* close to the bay, if they missed connections—that he might spend two or three days cruising about before leaving the coast behind him. There was a chance, then, that O'Reilly might be able to make the contact himself. Certainly it would be better to try, rather than to wait alone in the sandy valley and perhaps be recaptured before sundown.

Small game was plentiful along the shore. He used his knife to kill two possums and a pair of kangaroo rats. Their meat would be moist, and he hadn't a drop of water to ease his thirst. He carried the dead animals down to the shore and used a vine rope to tie them over the stern of the boat, to keep the meat from rotting in the blaze of the hot sun. Then he climbed aboard and shoved off, and began rowing on a straight course, heading out for the open sea.

All day long he rowed, without seeing a trace of the *Vigilant*. Nightfall found him far from land and far from Geographe Bay. He was well out on the Indian Ocean, exhausted by the heat of the afternoon and the weight of the oars. And that night he slept restlessly, stretched out in the bottom of the rolling boat, with only a piece of raw possum in his stomach for food and drink.

By sunrise even the possum meat and the kangaroo rats were gone. The sharks had taken them during the night. He rowed aimlessly all the next morning, wondering how long his strength would hold out, wondering if the prison guards would be waiting for him back on shore—if ever he did get back to shore. Finally, at noon, he sighted the far-off sails of the *Vigilant* and he pulled in his oars and sat waiting for her to draw near. There was no sense, he told himself, in trying to row close to her at that distance, or in trying to intercept her course. Either her lookouts would spot him, or they wouldn't. There was nothing more he could do. He could only wait and pray.

And for the second time they failed to see him. The full-sailed ship drew so near at one time that he was sure he could hear the shouts of a bosun, working a crew on deck. He could make out the features of a man aloft on the lookout. But all he could do was to sit bitterly in his boat, waving his shirt in hopeless, angry gestures. It was useless to shout, for the *Vigilant* was to the windward of him, and his voice only went drifting off across the sea in the wrong direction.

He wanted to weep, as he watched her sail off toward the horizon again, growing smaller each minute. But somehow he couldn't even do that. The tears refused to come.

He spent another night at sea, too weary and disconsolate even to try the oars. Next morning he awoke refreshed by the cool night air, and he spent all that day rowing back to shore. He made the boat secure on the beach, and he stumbled off to his secluded sandy valley. There he fell on the ground in despair, and finally he was able to weep, and so he fell asleep that way.

Five long days went by before Maguire and Mallory got

back from Bunbury. When at last they came, they brought
fresh hope. Maguire, with an encouraging smile, handed him
a letter from Father Mac. O'Reilly grabbed it eagerly, and
sat on the sand to read it:

DEAR JOHN: The ship *Gazelle* sails tomorrow. Captain
Gifford knows where you are and will put in toward the
coast at that point to take you on board. I've given him ten
pounds, to pay for your passage. But he says the passage
will be free, and the ten pounds will be for you. You'll need
it in America.

One unpleasant thing to mention: a convict named Martin
Bowman found out about your plan. You'll remember him—
probably the worst man in the Vasse. He would have killed
Tom Kelly if Kelly hadn't told him where you were heading. Bowman fled a search party and came to me and threatened to disclose everything to the police unless I guaranteed
him safe conduct to your hideout. I'm sorry, John, but that's
the way it had to be.

Fair winds, and a safe voyage to your new home. Remember me in your prayers. FATHER MAC.

O'Reilly finished the letter and looked up.

"Where's Bowman?" he asked Maguire.

"We left him back in the swamp there, with my cousins
guarding him. Shall we do him in?" Maguire looked as
though he'd enjoy the job.

O'Reilly shook his head slowly. "No. It wouldn't be fair
to Father Mac. And perhaps there's some good in the man
that we know nothing about. Bring him out here—we'll have
to take him along."

Maguire shrugged. "Whatever you say. You're the one
that has to sail with him. Now let's get to sea. We've got
plenty of water and plenty of food, and we'll all be safer out
of sight of land than we'll be sitting here. The whole country's swarming with guards out looking for you."

This time the contact was easy. Toward evening, far out on Geographe Bay, they saw the *Gazelle* and the *Vigilant* together, coming around the headland under full sail.

They saw the *Gazelle* abruptly change course and bear down in their direction while the *Vigilant* went on alone. The whaler came foaming across the miles, never swerving, until at last she was within hailing distance.

O'Reilly could see the sailors lining the rail and hanging on to the rigging. Some of them were shouting and waving their hats. He began to grin, and he reached across and poked Maguire on the knee.

"My new countrymen!" he said, gesturing at the crew.

"God bless them!" said Maguire.

He saw a big man on the quarterdeck pick up a megaphone, and then he heard a strong shout come ringing across the water.

"John Boyle O'Reilly! Ahoy, there!"

O'Reilly stood up in the boat and waved his arms.

The voice bellowed at him again. "I'm Captain Gifford, sir! Come aboard!"

That night, in the public places of Western Australia, the police nailed up a new notice. Copies were dispatched to all British colonies and to ports of call.

ABSCONDER

John Boyle O'Reilly, registered No. 9843, imperial convict; arrived in the colony per convict ship *Hougoumont* in 1868; sentenced to twenty years, 9th July 1866. Description— Healthy appearance; present age 25 years; 5 feet 7½ inches high, black hair, brown eyes, oval visage, dark complexion: an Irishman. Absconded from Convict Road Party, Bunbury, on the 18th of February, 1869.

17. YANKEE SHIPMATES

BOYLE O'REILLY stood leaning on the rail of the *Gazelle* as the trim bark quickly put about and pointed her nose toward the open sea. Suddenly the ship was a hive of action, of bellowed orders and answering cries, of slatting lines and cracking sails. He was aboard now, and the idea was to get far from land as quickly as possible, and to vanish into the vastness of the Indian Ocean.

He leaned on the rail with his arm upraised in a long gesture of farewell, and he held his eyes on Maguire's answering wave until the Irishman's dory began to fade in the distance and the sound of water rushing along the *Gazelle's* planks drowned out his last faint call of "God bless you!"

Then, with a speed that made him dizzy, O'Reilly felt a surging sense of freedom rush through his heart. He looked aloft, at the clean spread of white sails and at the outline of the masts swaying against the sky. He caught the song of the wind as it raced through the rigging. He stared down at the clean deck, freshly scrubbed and holystoned, and then back aft to where the American flag rippled and snapped above the ship's wake. He felt tears of relief and joy and gratitude filling his eyes, and he made no attempt to wipe them away. They belonged to the moment. Off in the distance the land was dropping back—the outline of Geographe Bay, with Cape Naturaliste and Cape Freycinet fading off in the sunlight. With every lift and plunge of the ship the Bush and the chains and the road gangs fell farther behind. He stood transfixed at the rail, staring back at the land where he had suffered so much.

His thoughts were interrupted by a quiet voice at his elbow. "We're well under way now, sir. Captain Gifford wants to see you."

O'Reilly turned with an apology. The man beside him was about his own age, barely an inch taller, a little heavier through the chest and shoulders, a man with dark, friendly eyes and with his hand outstretched.

"I'm Hathaway—third mate. Welcome aboard."

O'Reilly grasped his hand. "I'm sorry—I was lost in my own thoughts. You're the man that helped me up from the dory, aren't you? I shouldn't have kept you standing here so long."

Hathaway shrugged. "It was the best place for you. The others were pretty busy there for a while. Come along now, and meet the captain." He started across the deck.

O'Reilly followed him to the quarterdeck, where Gifford and one of his officers stood bending over a chart. Both men raised their heads with a look of welcome. The captain held out his hand and smiled broadly.

"Glad to have you with us, Mister O'Reilly. This is my first officer, Mister Hussey—Fred Hussey of New Bedford. You've met Mister Hathaway. Matter of fact, he was the man who lifted you out of the dory back there."

"Thank you, Captain," O'Reilly said. "Thank you for my life, all of you. I'd like to say more—but right now I can't."

He liked the way they looked—their leathery, tanned faces, the roll of their legs when they moved, the amused glint in their eyes as though the swift rescue maneuver were something that would give them entertaining talk for weeks to come.

Captain Gifford was speaking again. "We'll be occupied out here for a while, Mister O'Reilly. Got a lot of work to do and a lot of miles to cover. We'll all get acquainted later. Meanwhile, you look like you could use some rest."

It struck O'Reilly suddenly that he must look strangely out of place aboard the taut, clean ship. He noticed Gifford and Hussey looking him over with silent sympathy, and he realized what they were seeing—unkempt hair, sunken eyes, skin burned and blistered by the sun, convict clothes torn and ripped, knuckles scraped. Involuntarily his hand went up to his face and touched his stubbled chin as though in apology. It had been so long since he'd had a chance to shave, it seemed almost another lifetime.

Gifford gave him an understanding smile. "Don't let it bother you, Mister. We weren't looking to pick up a clothes horse. Go along with Mister Hathaway and get yourself some rest now. When you're feeling fit and alive, we'll sit and do some talking."

"Thank you, Captain." He turned and went with Hathaway, following the third mate off the quarterdeck and down the ladder to the officers' quarters.

Hathaway's stateroom was small, but after years of prison life it seemed to O'Reilly to hold limitless reaches of freedom. He stood in the center of the room and watched the mate pour two glasses of rum, and he looked around him in contentment. He liked what he saw. The shelves on one bulkhead held rows of books—poems, novels, biographies, navigation rules, tables of mathematics. There were dividers and a sextant on a small desk in one corner, a spyglass in a case, boots and heavy shirts hanging from hooks and swaying gently with the roll of the ship, a pistol and holster, a basket of fresh fruit. O'Reilly had almost forgotten that men could live like this.

Hathaway turned and held out a glass of rum and gestured

for him to sit down. From where he sat, on the edge of the narrow bunk, he could look beyond the mate's head through an open porthole and see the slow rise and fall of the horizon and hear the singing rush of water along the hull. He sighed contentedly, and answered Hathaway's upraised glass, and took a swallow of his drink.

"Just a couple of things to say," Hathaway told him, leaning back, "and then I'll leave you alone—and you can take all the time you want about coming out on deck again."

"Thanks," said O'Reilly. "It feels like a dream—as though it's not real."

Hathaway handed him a cigar. "Smoke this while I'm talking. Maybe that'll make it more real. By the way, they call me Henry.

"Now then—we talked this all over last night. The captain and Mister Hussey and me. Captain Gifford told me to tell you about it as soon as you were safe on board, because we've got to be ready for anything that might happen."

O'Reilly nodded, waiting.

"The British aren't going to cross you off and forget you with a snap of their fingers," Hathaway explained. "Sooner or later they'll find out we picked you up. Maybe they suspect it already. Anyhow, they'll be looking for you in every port where they have an agent, and the *Gazelle* will touch a lot of those ports before we see the States again.

"It would have been a lot easier if there'd been just you. But you know what happened back in Bunbury—that other man, Bowman, shoved himself into the picture." He curled his mouth in contempt.

"Where is he now?" O'Reilly wanted to know.

"Up in the fo'c'sle with the crew," Hathaway said. "You're a guest passenger—but not him. He's worse than a stowaway, and he's got to work for every mile we carry him. He came aboard with a sneer and a curse. We don't like that. By the time he gets off this ship, he'll think his job in the convict gang was easy.

"He makes it risky, though. He's a troublemaker, and he'd turn you in for a penny. So we've got to be careful when we're in port—wherever it is."

O'Reilly nodded. "He never did like me."

Hathaway freshened his drink. "The captain assigned me to stay with you as much as you'll have me. Any time you want to be alone, just say so. But anything else you want, I'm told to get it for you. I guess we'll get along. You'll bunk in here with me, you know."

O'Reilly looked around, wondering, and Hathaway laughed.

"That's a job for tomorrow," he explained. "We'll get another bunk built in here somehow.

"Anyhow, we plan to drop Bowman as soon as we can, if we can do it without putting you in danger. We'll leave him behind at some port somewhere. We promised him nothing, so that's exactly what he'll get—nothing but hard work, I mean.

"In your case, any time we're in port your name's Brown—John Brown. That's the name of a man we had with us till a couple of months ago. He died. We buried him at sea, in the Sunda Straits. He looked a lot like you. The captain says to tell you that's mighty important—that you're John Brown of New Bedford. And here are the papers he had with him." He held out a sealed envelope.

"I understand," O'Reilly agreed. He took the package.

Hathaway went on. "Don't ever worry about us standing by you. No telling when we'll get back to the States, but we'll try to keep you on the *Gazelle* all the way. If things get too warm—if the British start searching too close—Captain

Gifford says he'll hail another American whaler and put you aboard. But one way or another you'll get to the States. Believe me, you will. That's what we promised Father Mac, and we're going through with it."

O'Reilly felt his eyes fill a little with gratitude. It had been a long time since anyone had talked to him like this—offering him help and friendship—without the shadows of prison looming close at hand. He liked Hathaway, liked his frankness and understanding and generosity. Already he felt as though they'd known each other for a long time and had full trust in each other. And it would be the same way, he knew, with Gifford and Hussey—probably with all the other men aboard. He recalled how they had waved and cheered as the dory approached the *Gazelle,* and how two seamen had held Hathaway around the hips while he leaned far over and picked O'Reilly out of the small tossing boat. And he recalled, too, the speed and spirit with which all hands had turned to their work then, swinging the bark hard about on her course and starting up a chantey as she turned foaming toward the open sea.

So these were Americans! He was going to be happy with them.

He reached out and clasped Hathaway's hand.

"There's a great deal to say," he explained. "But I can't say it now. Two reasons, I guess—too much emotion, for one thing, and too much weariness for another. I'm very tired, Henry. All of a sudden I'm more tired than I've ever been in my life."

Hathaway smiled, clapped him on the shoulder, and got to his feet. "You've been living a long time on nerve, John. Relax—let everything go, and relax. Weep if you feel like it. We'd understand."

"I'm going to."

"Are you hungry? Want something to eat?"

O'Reilly shook his head. "Suddenly all I want is to sleep."

"That's good. It's a good sign." Hathaway took his glass and his cigar and put them aside. "I've got to go on watch for the next four hours. This is your home now, John, so make it that way. There's water in the pitcher, if you want to clean up. Help yourself to the razor and the soap. Strip off those dirty convict rags and throw them out the porthole, and then take whatever clothes you need out of my gear. We're about the same size—most of my stuff'll fit you. I'll look in on you four hours from now."

O'Reilly nodded, suddenly too weary even to speak. He watched Hathaway leave the room and saw the door close behind him, and then for several long minutes he sat motionless on the edge of the bunk, staring dazedly at the porthole and watching the rise and fall of the horizon line. He felt that he should pray, and say thanks to God for leading him back again to freedom. But he knew that if he got on his knees and closed his eyes even for an instant he'd fall into a deep sleep. He felt, too, that he should wash the dirt of the Bush swamps from his body, and shave, and sponge the dried blood from where it had caked on his scratched and broken skin. But he knew that he was too weak. With the agony of the past days behind him, suddenly he felt drained of all strength and as helpless and feeble as a newborn kitten.

He would pray later—and wash the dirt and the aches from his body—and sit with Captain Gifford and Hathaway and the others later, and tell them what this meant to him. He would do all that—later——

He lay down with his head on the pillow of the bunk, and in a matter of moments he was in a deep sleep.

Four hours later Henry Hathaway came off watch and stepped quietly into the room. He looked down at O'Reilly and listened a while to his heavy breathing and smiled a little with sympathy. It was dark outside by now, and the stars shone through the open port, and the cool night air was streaming in. Hathaway took a blanket from his drawer and put it over O'Reilly. Then, without lighting the lamp, he took off his sea jacket and folded it into a pillow and stretched out on the floor of the cabin with his head resting against his sea chest, and fell asleep that way.

O'Reilly was still asleep and breathing heavily when Hathaway went back on watch after another four hours.

But the next time he came back to the cabin, he saw that sometime during the hours O'Reilly had awakened and had taken a sponge bath and a shave. The convict clothes were gone, and he noticed that O'Reilly had climbed back under the blanket naked and refreshed and was sleeping easily now, with a peaceful look on his face. Hathaway turned to his desk, and found a short note pinned there:

"Henry—I'm feeling much better now. Going back for more sleep. Dr. Johnson once said, 'Being on a ship is like being in a jail with a chance of being drowned.' He was ignorant on both counts—jails and ships alike. Boyle O'Reilly."

Hathaway laughed to himself. This, he decided, was going to be a stimulating voyage.

18. "WHITE WATER"

THE *Gazelle* beat north-northwest up the coast of Australia for a final three-month swing through whaling waters before heading home. Below the horizon to the east Fremantle slipped by unseen, and Carnarvon, and Northwest Cape. And then the bark pointed her nose toward the Sunda Strait.

She sailed into the narrow gap one sundown, and when the moon rose that night O'Reilly stood on deck and watched the beauty of its yellow light on the jungles of Java off to starboard and of Sumatra off to port. The canvas flapped gently, and at one time the *Gazelle* sailed so close to land that he could hear the scream of a tiger rising out across the water from the dark forest.

Still northward they sailed, through good whaling grounds, into the Malay Archipelago and the Java Sea. They crossed the equator going north through Karimata Strait, and then rounded Borneo and crossed the line again heading south, down through the Sulu Archipelago and the Celebes Sea.

During all those days and nights Boyle O'Reilly felt his health and strength coming back, along with an impatient desire to be more active—to be more a part of the *Gazelle's* life than just a non-paying passenger without a home. From time to time he worried a little about what might happen when the ship dropped anchor in some British port. With that thought in mind, he stopped shaving and grew a beard for disguise. It was thick and black and bristly, and he became quite proud of it.

He was drawn close to the men around him, especially to

Gifford and Hathaway, and they liked him. They sat with him off watch, swapping tales of New England and Yankee shipping for tales of Ireland and English prisons. They taught him sea chanteys, and he sang the old songs of Ireland in trade. They drank the captain's rum and smoked his cigars.

"It's a good voyage," Gifford said, passing the drinks around. "Plenty of oil for the owners. Not an empty barrel aboard by the time we round the Cape. We'll all make money this trip."

They set out finally to make a real sailor of O'Reilly. They assigned him a place in Hathaway's boat, and he learned to jump fast when the lookout at the masthead yelled "She blows!" He learned to swing his oar and to stay clear of the harpooneer as a great sperm broke the sea.

And so they moved slowly south through the good whaling waters, working hard by day, rowing over to visit other Yankee ships by night when the waters were calm and the crews worked the dead whales by the light of smoking, ruddy fires.

And then one day they had sailed as far south again as the Timor Sea, and dead ahead loomed the north coast of Australia and the outstretched arm of Cape Londonderry. And at high noon that day, with the *Gazelle* sliding through the waves, Captain Gifford picked up his megaphone and shouted the order the crew had been waiting to hear.

"Hard right rudder! Steady as she goes! Look sharp for Nantucket!"

The *Gazelle* swung about like a thing alive, and seemed to shake herself a moment, as though gathering strength. Then she plunged off due west, heading for the vast reaches that lay across the Indian Ocean.

"An extra ration of grog for all hands!"

The crew cheered and broke into a loud chantey. The *Gazelle* had begun her long voyage toward home. Captain

Gifford put his megaphone aside, glanced up at the sun, and wrote a new entry into the log.

Hathaway and O'Reilly, standing together at the rail, turned for a last look at Australia. They left the rail to join Captain Gifford for a drink of rum. Somewhere ahead lay New England and the end of the journey, halfway around the world.

It was two days later, with the ship gliding through a swelling sea, when O'Reilly's part in the voyage almost came to an abrupt end, and with it, Hathaway's as well. It was a day for lazing on deck, with a warm May sun shining down from an azure sky. The *Gazelle* was running smoothly in a quartering wind, her sails gleaming white and her flags rippling with color. Up forward the seamen off watch were listening to the song of a Kanaka harpooneer trying to trap his island melody in the notes of a Yankee accordion. The ship's carpenter was working on an outrigger model, sanding its hull gently. Even Martin Bowman, despised by every man in the fo'c'sle, had come out on deck to lie in the sun at the edge of the group. It was a day for warm, peaceful hours and putting the miles astern. Then, suddenly, it was a day for swift action and high courage. Three lookouts were aloft. Their yells came down with such suddenness that they sounded almost like one voice:

"She blows!"

"—blows! Dead ahead!"

"—blows! White waters! Three points port bow!"

The shouts sprung the ship into action. Captain Gifford leaped up with his glass, sweeping the seas ahead.

The lookouts were yelling from aloft again:

"Two miles to port, Captain! Moving away fast!"

"White waters ahead! Maybe another!"

The *Gazelle* had come upon a school of four whales—

maybe five—and all sperm. The men rushed for the boats, stood there waiting, tense and excited.

Captain Gifford swung about and shouted his orders: "Swing the boats! Stand by to lower! Steersman, come left three points—left, damn it! Hold her there! Ready with the boats—lower away!"

The lines sang through the falls. The boats hit the water almost with a single slap. Oars flashed out, and the whale crews pulled away from the *Gazelle* with a speed that whirled the water in their wake.

In Hathaway's boat, O'Reilly strained at his oar with all his power. He grinned at the third mate, and caught an answering grin back. This was the way to live—freedom, excitement, action—sharing it with Negro, white man, Kanaka—all pulling together, all with one goal! The *Gazelle* fell behind them. The seas between widened.

He saw their quarry then. It was a monstrous thing, rolling in the swells some two miles away, spurting a high stream into the sunlight, and rolling again with a sighing snort. The boat moved closer and closer, shortening the gap that lay between. They drew near, and Hathaway studied the whale and knew they'd have a battle on their hands. His harpooneer glanced around, thin-lipped, and raised his eyes in mock alarm. He pretended to shiver with fright. Hathaway gestured at him to stand alert and keep his irons ready. He motioned to his steersman to come left a little—then steady. He spoke quietly to the boat crew.

"That's it, boys—softly. Hold 'er right there—now, in with the oars. Up forward, there—ready with the irons?"

"Aye, sir," almost a whisper.

"He's a monster. He'll take two."

"Two, sir—aye."

"Steady now—on the next roll. *Heave! Again!*"

The harpoons flashed out like flung spears, one behind the other, with incredible speed. The first one struck, buried its barb, quivered, and held fast. The second one struck but slipped, and hung there swaying.

The crew grabbed gunwales and seats, bracing for the expected foaming ride across the waves. O'Reilly stared ahead excitedly with the rest, ready for the whale to sound. All in an instant he saw the harpoons strike, the crew snap taut, and then he heard a shout of horror from Hathaway.

"God! Look out! He's attacking!"

Like a giant black demon, the great whale swirled around and plunged straight for the boat. No sounding, no racing flight—just an abrupt, head-on rush through the waters to batter this thing that had stung him.

As one man the crew leaped for the waves. But not soon enough. O'Reilly had a fleeting glimpse of something tremendous and black crashing down upon him, churning the sea to destruction. Then the whale's giant flukes hit the boat. O'Reilly was unconscious before he was under the water.

Hathaway leaped, just ahead of the impact. He surfaced in the middle of a scene of wreckage. The boat was a shambles. Broken oars and splinters of wood swirled here and there. Men were floundering around grasping at anything that could float. A piece of the stern, some ten feet long, rushed past Hathaway's head on the curl of a wave. He grabbed it and clung to it. He looked around wildly. The whale was gone.

"Where's O'Reilly!" he shouted.

A frantic voice: "I see him, mate! Under that plank there!"

Somehow, Hathaway got to his side with the stern piece still in tow and grabbed him by his hair. He was unconscious, badly hurt, with a bloody froth running from his nose and mouth. For an instant Hathaway thought he was dead, but he

saw a quiver of life at the corner of O'Reilly's mouth. He
held O'Reilly with one hand, while he heaved himself up
to the surface of the wreckage with the other. Then he rolled
O'Reilly up after him, and they lay there together, with the
waves washing over them. And that was the way they stayed.

The time seemed endless before anyone came to their rescue. Bit by bit the survivors of the whaleboat drifted farther
and farther apart, until Hathaway was alone with O'Reilly on
his wreckage and could see no other trace of life on the sea.
He noticed with dismay that the wind had shifted and was
carrying them away from where they had left the *Gazelle* so
long ago. He lifted himself as high as he dared and shaded his
eyes from the sun, but there was no sail in sight and no whaleboat in sight.

They were awash on the makeshift raft, submerged in every wave that came along. Over and over again the water
rushed down on them, plunging them under. Each time they
emerged, Hathaway punched O'Reilly's stomach to keep him
from swallowing salt. Each time he wiped his friend's face,
shook his own head, and braced for the next wave. And so it
went, again and again, in a torture of endless time and growing weariness, until at last the day was old and Hathaway
was so weak he could barely keep a grip on O'Reilly's shirt
and barely move his hand to wipe his eyes.

They were that way four hours later, when finally a rescue
boat from the *Gazelle* sighted them and bore down on them
with swift oars. O'Reilly was still unconscious when they
lifted him aboard. And the last thing Hathaway remembered
hearing was some comment about wasting time with a dead
man, and then seeing somebody's hand reach down to take
his burden from him. Then he, too, lost consciousness.

It was much later when he opened his eyes again. He was
in his own bunk and he felt surprised at seeing the familiar

things of his cabin. He couldn't remember being brought back aboard. He looked up and saw O'Reilly, sitting beside him, leaning over with an anxious light in his eyes, and he saw the look change to mixed sympathy and relief.

O'Reilly reached out and placed a hand on his shoulder tenderly. His voice was gentle. "Henry, why didn't you let me go? Why didn't you let me go?"

Hathaway tried to smile. "You've too much to live for. And we're friends."

He fell unconscious again. It was another two days before he was able to sit up and talk.

And it was another two weeks before either of them could move about well enough to get back into the swing of the ship's routine. O'Reilly had been badly battered by the crashing flukes of the whale, and Hathaway had been worn close to the point of death by his hours on the splintered raft.

In those two weeks, though, they built fresh life into a friendship that already had been warm. And O'Reilly, more than ever before, longed eagerly to be a part of a country that could turn out men like this—not like Hathaway alone, but like Gifford, too, and Fred Hussey, and the bosun who carved ship models for his grandchildren, and the seamen who lived in harmony with men of other races, and the harpooneers who dared to match their skill and bravery against the big whales, and the steersmen who sang of home and New England while watching the stars at night.

It was good to be on his way to America with such men. Sometimes during those hours, while he sat and watched Hathaway asleep and recovering, he would say his thanks in prayer, and weep quietly out of gratitude.

19. HALF MAST AT RODERIQUE

SOMEWHERE, sooner or later, they were bound to come looking for O'Reilly. He knew they would never give up the search. The warning had gone out from Fremantle months before, telegraphed to all British ports where an escaped convict might touch, calling for a careful scrutiny of the men aboard American vessels in particular. The Government wanted O'Reilly and Bowman back in the swamps of the Vasse. Their recapture and the punishment that would follow would be a warning to other convicts to obey the rules.

The word had reached the small British island of Roderique, in the Indian Ocean, and had almost been forgotten in the passing of the months. Then one day it was brought to the attention of the island's governor, as the *Gazelle* rounded a headland and entered the harbor and signaled that she would take a fresh supply of water and food on board.

The governor watched through his glass as the ship furled sails and dropped her anchor. He saw a party put off toward shore in a small boat and head for the customs shed. There went the captain, he supposed, and one or two mates. He decided he'd better check on the other men aboard. The warm July sun was low in the sky, almost touching the horizon, and he'd just about have time to make the inspection and get back ashore for dinner. He rapped the bell on his desk, and told an aide to assemble an armed police guard quickly and have a boat standing by at the dock.

O'Reilly and Hathaway watched from the *Gazelle* and saw the boat put out from shore. They had expected something of the sort to happen. They had talked with Captain Gifford about the risk when they'd first sighted Roderique, hours before. But the call had to be made; the *Gazelle* couldn't go on without fresh water and supplies.

Captain Gifford had mentioned it briefly again, just before going over the side to his waiting boat.

"You're in command, Mister Hathaway. I'll be back in the morning. If any visitors arrive for Mister Brown, show them the courtesy they deserve."

"Aye, sir—the courtesy they deserve."

They watched now from the *Gazelle* as the governor's boat came swiftly toward them across the water. Hathaway tossed a dead cigar into the harbor.

"You have your papers handy, Mister Brown?"

O'Reilly touched his hip pocket. "I do, Mister Hathaway. Aye, sir, that is. Looks as though the gentleman's bringing the island militia to help him."

"Ummmm." Hathaway nodded. "And he wouldn't need a single man, either. Poor O'Reilly—I remember him well. He always was afraid something like this would happen."

"I know. I think that's what drove him to jump overboard. Poor fellow."

A shout came from the governor's boat, swinging alongside. "Permission to come aboard, sir?"

"Permission granted," Hathaway called down.

He and O'Reilly stood by the rail and gave the governor a hand as he came up the ladder. The armed guards followed and moved restlessly across the deck.

The governor didn't bother with introductions, but plunged directly into the business at hand. "You're in command, I suppose. Your captain's ashore? Tell me, do you have a man on board named John Boyle O'Reilly?"

"O'Reilly?" Hathaway frowned and looked puzzled.

"He's an absconder from Fremantle," the governor said.

"A dangerous criminal. A man about your height—black hair, brown eyes—carries himself like a soldier. We're looking for him and another absconder named Martin Bowman. Thought they might have stowed away on your ship at Bunbury. Know anything about it?"

O'Reilly spoke up. "Mister Hathaway, what about that man who jumped overboard?"

"Sure enough." Hathaway nodded. "That could have been O'Reilly, Governor. He answered that description. We found him aboard after we sailed from Bunbury. He leaped overboard one night in the Sunda Strait. Poor fellow, I don't think he had a chance of making the shore. We never saw him again."

"I see." The governor stared at Hathaway for several moments, and then looked curiously at O'Reilly, as though wondering what the face looked like behind the black beard. Then he looked back at Hathaway again. "Now then—you're in British waters, you know. My position here gives me authority to call for a muster of the crew. Have them turned out on deck, sir. I'll have to see every man aboard."

Hathaway turned and shouted an order to the deck watch. A moment later men came hurrying from the fo'c'sle.

They lined up on the starboard side, facing outboard— Yankees and Portuguese, whites and blacks, islanders from Nantucket and islanders from the Azores, proud New Bedford sons and half-breed Cape Cod Indians—a typical Yankee whaling crew. Martin Bowman stood among them, still with the trace of a sneer on his lips but also now with a look of fright growing in his eyes. And beside him, smiling to himself, stood a small galley boy who had been bullied and tormented by Bowman since the ship had left Bunbury.

The governor led his group along the line, staring intently into each face, looking the men up and down and comparing them with the descriptions of the convicts. His armed police followed close behind, ready to seize any man who might break for the rail. Nobody spoke. The *Gazelle* was silent, except for the light sound of a rope swaying in the breeze against the mainmast—that and the slow steps of the British officer.

The governor reached Bowman and paused. Bowman stared straight ahead. After a moment the governor passed on. He stopped again, in front of the galley boy. The boy stood rigid, with his gaze frozen. The officer was about to move along, then halted for just an instant. From the corner of his eye he caught a barely perceptible jerk of the boy's thumb. It twitched briefly toward Bowman, then the boy was rigid again.

Nobody in the line could have seen the giveaway gesture. O'Reilly, standing by the rail, caught sight of it, and knew instantly what it would mean. He watched the governor move on down the line as though nothing had happened, and he felt grateful toward the man for not betraying the boy in front of Bowman.

The inspection ended. The governor halted at the far limit of the line. He looked back up the row of men, still standing rigid with their eyes on the horizon. He spoke under his breath to his police squad. The men moved swiftly down the deck, straight to Bowman, and grabbed him by the arms. "Come along, convict!" Bowman started to shout a protest. One of the guards clapped a big hand across his mouth. In a flash they hustled him across the deck to the rail and started him down the side.

At the last instant he managed to twist around in their grip and glare directly at O'Reilly. "Good-by, *shipmate!*" he cried. He swore loudly as they punched and wrestled him down the ladder and into the waiting boat.

The governor hesitated—staying behind an instant. He stared thoughtfully at O'Reilly. Then he jerked his head and turned quickly to Hathaway. "Thank you for your help, sir."

He followed the guards over the side, and in another minute the boat was moving away toward shore and the crew of the *Gazelle* stood along the rail watching it go. Then the bosun ordered them all below except the anchor watch.

The boat pulled out of earshot, and O'Reilly turned hurriedly to Hathaway. For the first time in months his eyes held their old hunted look again.

"Henry!" He grabbed the mate's arm. "You know what's going to happen! Bowman singled me out—they'll remember that! Once he gets ashore he'll try to turn me in. But I won't go back, Henry! They won't get me back there alive. I'll take pistols and shoot it out with them!"

Hathaway put a hand on his shoulder and calmed him down. "Easy, John—cool off there, friend. Cool off. Sure Bowman's going to start talking, as soon as he thinks he can make a deal for himself. But nobody's taking you back to Australia, O'Reilly, and there won't be any shooting. Now let's just think this thing out. Let's find a way to lick it."

They paced up and down the deck in silence, groping for ideas. The sun had disappeared, and the dark twilight shadows were covering the harbor. Lights were beginning to appear in the small houses on land.

"We'd better hurry," O'Reilly said. "It'll be dark in a few minutes, and we wouldn't see them coming back."

Hathaway stopped abruptly and snapped his fingers in triumph. "Darkness! Exactly!"

"Exactly what?"

The mate grinned. "That's the hideaway—the darkest place on ship. Nobody'll ever find you there. It's a hidden crockery locker, right under the companionway to the main cabin, and the only way to get in is by taking off a plank on one of the steps and squeezing down.

"Listen now, if they come back at all tonight, it won't be for some time yet. The tide's low. I think you're safe for the next few hours. Get down to the stateroom while I get things ready. I don't want anyone to see you around with me and suspect what's going on."

It was close to midnight when O'Reilly heard the mate come quietly into the cabin. He'd kept the room in darkness and was stretched out on the bunk with Hathaway's pistol in his hand. Hathaway struck a match and lit the cabin lamp.

"Put the gun away," he said. "We won't need that. You ready for the hideout?"

"Ready." O'Reilly swung his legs over the edge of the bunk and sat up. He tossed the pistol aside carelessly. "I feel better now, Henry. I'm sorry about the way I behaved on deck. It won't happen again."

"No. Don't apologize—not after what they did to you. Now, then, get your hat. The old slouch thing that the crew sees you wearing all the time. Has it got your name in it— your number too, eh? Good. Here's what we're going to do. You come with me first to see just where the plank is loose. I took out the screws. I could barely squeeze inside, so I know you can make it. You're thinner than I am. Come along now —I'll tell you the rest of the plan when we get there. And don't forget the hat."

Half an hour later Hathaway sauntered forward along the starboard deck, a mate on duty with nothing to do. He gazed idly out to sea, and tapped his fingers on the rail. After a while he walked on again, still going forward. He stopped at a windlass to talk with the anchor watch. O'Reilly crouched out of sight in the darkness, close to the head of the companionway. He stared sharply in both directions, to make

sure the deck was not being watched. Then he reached behind him and picked up a heavy grindstone wheel. He squat-
ted there on his heels, holding tightly to the grindstone and
to his old slouch hat. He kept his eyes on Hathaway, waiting
for the signal to move.

Hathaway kept on talking to the seamen. It seemed like
forever. But finally he pulled out a cigar and struck a match.
The signal!

O'Reilly leaped quickly to the rail, screamed wildly,
heaved the grindstone and the hat into the sea, and jumped
back down the darkness of the companionway.

The scream and the splash startled every man aboard ship.

Hathaway rushed to the rail, swung about, and bellowed
the alarm:

"Man overboard! All hands! All hands! Man the boats!
Bring lanterns!"

Below, O'Reilly jerked to a halt on the steps, grabbed the
loose board, and hurriedly squeezed himself into the locker,
pulling the board tight above him. Overhead, he heard the
furious racing of feet, the shouts of alarm, the screech of the
falls as the boats hit the water.

Dimly, muffled through the planking, he could even hear
the shouts carrying from boat to boat.

"Who was it? Anyone know? O'Reilly! I heard him scream!
I saw him jump, mate! He looked crazy. Poor O'Reilly! We'll
get him!"

The boats swept back and forth, all around the ship,
searching in the flaring light of lanterns. They dragged with
weighted ropes. They shouted his name over and over again.
They even fired pistols across the water, wondering if that
would bring his body to the surface. After a while Hathaway
heard an excited cry from one of the rescue crews, and he saw

through the lantern light that somebody had recovered the slouch hat.

"It's his!" came the shout. "His name's inside it. We got his hat!"

And after a long time, one by one, the boats came slowly back to the *Gazelle* and were hoisted aboard. Hathaway's conscience stabbed him at the sight of some of the men, weeping openly. He longed to tell them that Boyle O'Reilly was safe aboard, and that there'd be more songs and poetry and stories and laughs in another day or so. But he didn't dare. This was going to have to look genuine or the whole thing would fail.

And much later, when the ship was all quiet again for the night, Hathaway went on soft steps to the companionway and tapped gently on the loose plank.

He put his head close down and whispered.

"Everything all right, Boyle?"

"Good, Henry. Cramped but good."

"I brought along the loose screws to put back. There— you're in tight. Stay quiet now till I come and get you out, no matter how long you have to stay there."

"Thanks, Henry. And good night."

At sunrise the next morning the *Gazelle* raised the "man lost overboard" signal and flew an ensign flag at half-mast. Captain Gifford spotted it from the governor's office, let out a gasp of surprise, and turned to Fred Hussey beside him.

"You stay, Mister Hussey. There's a death aboard ship— I've got to get out there. You stay and finish the business with the governor."

He left on the run, thankful that the shore boat was manned and waiting for him. It was a long way down to the harbor's edge. He was panting for breath when he got there.

As he jumped aboard, he heard Hussey shouting after him through a megaphone from the steps of the government house.

"Governor says get that flag at full mast right away—dead man or no dead man!"

Captain Gifford frowned in shocked surprise. Then he shrugged. These were British waters. There was nothing he could do but obey orders. He turned to the boat crew.

"Pull away, boys. Pull hard!"

They told him the news aboard the *Gazelle*. He nearly collapsed when he heard it, and for a long moment he couldn't believe it. Then Hathaway pointed to O'Reilly's slouch hat, still damp from the sea, drying on the forward hatch.

"We did what we could, Captain. There wasn't a trace of him. Just the hat, drifting away from the ship."

Captain Gifford went straight to his cabin, to sit alone. He wanted to weep.

And the hat was still there on the hatch, an hour or so later, when the governor came out in the police boat. With him was Fred Hussey with the papers showing that the ship's business was finished and that she was cleared for sailing. And with him also was Martin Bowman. He had made his deal for a little clemency, and he was ready to point out O'Reilly and turn him in. The black look on the governor's face showed that he didn't enjoy making terms with a convict.

They pointed out the hat to him, and told him the story. He snorted with disbelief, and for a moment it looked as if he might demand a search of the ship. Then he stared from face to face at the men on deck. Some of them, returning from shore and hearing the story for the first time, had tears on their cheeks. Captain Gifford came on deck, looking ready to break down and weep openly. He appealed to the governor with his eyes to let them get away quickly and be by themselves.

The governor hesitated, and then nodded.

"You're ready for sea?"

"Ready," said Captain Gifford shortly.

"Safe voyage, then—and I'm sorry about all this. Truly sorry. These things happen in line of duty, and that's about all I can say." He held out his hand to the captain.

Then he was gone, over the side and down the ladder, with the police guards prodding Bowman ahead of them. The convict never looked back at the ship.

The windlass began to creak; the anchor came splashing up from the harbor bottom, dropping mud back into the waves; and the sails boomed out on the *Gazelle* as she swung away from land and headed back into the open sea. The shore was only a blue haze on the horizon when Hathaway finally took a screw driver and went back to the companionway. Without a tap or a word, he loosened the plank and lifted it off. O'Reilly squeezed out quickly, exhaling a deep breath and stretching his arms and legs. He was trembling a little.

"What now? Are we safe?"

Hathaway grinned and gave him a cigar. "Land's about out of sight. Go on up on deck and say hello to the captain. I'll be right behind you. I want to see this myself."

Captain Gifford was pacing back and forth on the quarterdeck with his head hanging low. O'Reilly approached him quietly.

"Good morning, sir. Good to be under way again."

Gifford leaped back with a startled shout. His face went white. Then he hurled himself forward and flung his arms around O'Reilly, and burst into unashamed tears.

"It's so good to see you alive, boy! So good to see you alive!"

Later that day Gifford sent for all of them to come to his quarters. He served coffee and rum, and they went over the angles of the incident.

At the end, Hathaway said, "Anyhow, that was one time the governor of Roderique got fooled. We really had him going."

Hussey looked across at O'Reilly. "Did we? Tell them, John."

O'Reilly shook his head at Hathaway. "Maybe we fooled him. Maybe not. Hussey stayed behind when the captain came aboard. Remember?"

"I remember." Hathaway looked puzzled.

"Well, Fred told me later what happened in the government house right after that. He said Bowman was dragged in and kept trying to shout something about me and my beard. And the governor ordered him to shut up—stay quiet—and threatened to have him gagged. So Bowman held his tongue. And then when the governor saw the *Gazelle's* flag at half-mast, he said, 'The damned fools—they'll have half a hundred men out there from shore, trying to dive for a body. And that's one thing they don't want.' That's when he sent the order after the captain, to get the flag up to full mast again."

Hathaway nodded. "Not fooled a bit, huh?"

O'Reilly reached for more coffee. "Like Fred Hussey said, the English are just like everybody else in every other country —some good, some bad. The governor happened to be one of the good ones."

Hussey broke in. "Also," he said, "the governor happens to have a wife who is very beautiful and very charming. I met her this morning. She's Irish, O'Reilly—comes from County Meath."

20. SHIPS THAT PASS

THE INCIDENT at Roderique worried them. If it happened again, the ending might be disastrous. For the next day or two nobody spoke of that possibility, but it was heavy on their minds.

To O'Reilly, the episode was proof that the British never would let up in their attempts to get him back. No matter how many months or years went by, and no matter how cold his trail might grow, they'd always be looking for him, always ready to seize him the instant he came, by land or sea, within reach of the British arm. For the present, he couldn't be certain that the Roderique case was closed. There were others on the island besides the governor and his wife. It would be easy for the story to find its way out. A question here or there, a comment, a careless word, perhaps, from one of the police guards, and the whole thing might break into the open. Perhaps that had happened already. If it had, it would mean the *Gazelle* was a marked ship, from now until the end of her voyage.

To Hathaway, the incident had brought home with a shock the realization of the dangers that would surround O'Reilly until he reached the States and freedom. Hathaway had grown to love the man. They'd spent long hours as shipmates and cabin mates, and there'd never been any friction between them. They had prayed together on their knees at night. They'd gone into deep discussions of poetry, books, celestial navigation, the origins of early Irish music, the principles of democratic government. They had speculated together about the future. They had even planned vaguely, someday, to outfit another whaling bark in New Bedford and sail her to Australia to rescue other Irish convicts from the road gangs. It would be a bleak voyage from here home, without O'Reilly aboard. But somehow Hathaway felt convinced that O'Reilly would not be safe much longer aboard the *Gazelle*.

As for Captain Gifford, he reminded himself that he had a responsibility to the ship's owners, and also in a sense to the United States Government. He couldn't afford to keep tangling with the British, challenging them to recover one of their own prisoners from him. If it meant saving O'Reilly's life he'd go on doing it gladly, in defiance of anyone in Washington or London or New Bedford or Boston. He liked O'Reilly well enough for that. But he sensed that things were closing in, and O'Reilly was in danger. They'd been lucky at Roderique. But had the story ended there? On their next stop, they'd be sailing straight into British hands again, at the Island of St. Helena. No, for O'Reilly's own sake, some way of protecting him would have to be found before they made that landfall.

And so Captain Gifford called them together to talk it over. They sat in his cabin, the three of them, and laid their thoughts and worries on the line and tried to plan a way out. Gifford chewed his cigar and sat with his feet braced against his bunk to offset the roll of the ship. Hathaway sat on the floor with his back against the captain's desk and tapped his fingers in thought. And O'Reilly sat beside him and tugged worriedly at his beard. There seemed to be only one thing to do, and none of them wanted to do it; that was to get O'Reilly off the *Gazelle* and onto another ship.

The captain frowned at his cigar smoke. "We haven't got any choice about it. The grindstone stunt was tricky, but we were loaded with luck. We can't go around throwing grindstones into the sea every time a British officer comes aboard

—not and expect to get away with it, anyhow. What do you think, Mister Hathaway?"

"I think we're stumped, Captain. That trick wouldn't work again. By now somebody must know what happened—and the story will go the rounds, wherever there's a British government house. I'd hate to see John leave the *Gazelle*, but he'd better. If he stays with us, they'll get him sure."

The captain nodded. "And how about you, Mister O'Reilly? You've got more of a stake in this than anybody. What's your line of thinking?"

O'Reilly was silent a moment. He clasped his hands over his knees. "A poet named Montgomery," he said, "once wrote what I'm thinking now. It went:

> "Friend after friend departs;
> Who hath not lost a friend?
> There is no union here of hearts
> That finds not here an end.

"I've found the best friends in the world here on the *Gazelle*. It's hard to think of leaving. But if I stay, and we get to St. Helena, I'll be putting all the rest of you in an awkward spot and causing real trouble. As for myself—I doubt if I'd stay free at St. Helena. They'd catch me there, I'm sure."

"Then it's all settled." Captain Gifford got to his feet and crossed to his chart table. He beckoned the other two to join him. "Here's our noon position today—this dot. We'll be off the Cape of Good Hope on the twenty-ninth. There'll be other American ships there—we can count on that—there's always somebody there, making the turn to start up the South Atlantic.

"We'll hail a north-bound Yankee ship and go aboard and tell the skipper the whole story. You won't have to worry, Mister O'Reilly—Yankee mariners know how to keep their mouths shut. They'd never spill your secret. So if it's agreeable all around, we'll transfer you on the twenty-ninth and wish you a safe voyage home."

O'Reilly nodded. "It's the only way."

"We'll even give you a new name," Gifford said, turning to his desk drawer. "Mister Hathaway, what was the name of that man who deserted at Capetown on the way out?"

"John Soule, sir."

"John Soule, yes—that was it. I have his record here somewhere. Ah, yes. Now, Mister O'Reilly or Mister Brown— when you go aboard your next ship you'll be John Soule. The skipper will be the only one that knows the real story, unless he finds it necessary to tell somebody else. Mister Hathaway will give you all the information you need about Soule to act the part right. And if the British go looking anywhere for John Brown—well, he just doesn't exist any more. He just this instant fell from a yardarm on the *Gazelle* and was lost at sea. What say, Mister Soule?"

"I say thanks," said O'Reilly dryly, "but I sense an insult in the background. First I'm a man who dives overboard in the Sunda Strait. Then I'm a man who deserts at Capetown. I'm beginning to suspect you're a character assassin, Captain Gifford. Or maybe you don't know any respectable Yankees."

"Fine words from a convict!" Gifford snorted. "One short drink now—success to John Soule. And we'll leave it at that till we're off the big Cape."

At midmorning on July 29 the masthead lookout reported a sail coming up fast from the starboard quarter. By noon, they could read its markings through the long glass. She was the bark *Sapphire,* out of Boston.

Captain Gifford lowered the glass and gave a deep sigh of relief. "Couldn't be better," he said. "I've known her master

for years—Captain Seiders. And there's nothing he likes better than playing tricks on the English. Mister Hathaway!"

"Aye, sir."

"Hoist the ensign to the mizzen peak and stand by for a
reply."

At sundown that night the ships lay to with a mile of open
water between them.

On the *Gazelle,* Hussey kept a glass trained on the Boston
bark, waiting for Gifford and Hathaway to return. O'Reilly,
he felt certain, would not be coming back. He cast an uneasy
glance at the western horizon. Clouds were making up heavily, just below the setting sun. They'd be in for a blow in a
day or two. It would be better to be clear of the Cape by then,
and out on the South Atlantic. Captain Gifford ought to get
the *Gazelle* under way. But then, Gifford certainly knew the
situation as well as anyone. Hussey turned his gaze back to
the other ship. She was a good-looking craft—speedy-looking
too—swifter than the *Gazelle.*

On the *Sapphire,* Captain Seiders leaned forward across his
desk and cupped his pipe in both hands and listened to the
end of the story. They'd been sitting in Seiders' cabin for
more than half an hour now, giving him the whole account,
all the happenings from the prisons of England to the grindstone at Roderique. And Seiders had been a good listener.
He'd broken in with a question or two now and then, but
for the most part he'd sat quietly and had let them handle
the story their own way. He'd glanced at O'Reilly from time
to time with an amused glint in his eyes, and then again with
a look of pity and sympathy. O'Reilly studied him and liked
him—a rugged man with a thick beard and a strong face.

Captain Gifford finished his story. "So there it is—that's
why we're here, to see if you'd help. We brought all his gear
along, on the chance that you'd take him."

Seiders put his pipe aside and reached in his desk for a bottle. "Was there ever any question? Of course I'll take him. Leave him with me and he'll be safe. I'll see to that. Mister O'Reilly?" He held out a jigger of brandy and then passed some to Gifford and Hathaway.

"Mister Soule, I suppose I should say, just to get the habit. At any rate, you'll share this cabin with me. There's plenty of room for both of us. And as far as the men aboard the *Sapphire* are concerned, you're an old friend of mine and you're my personal guest for the rest of the voyage. Here's luck and fair winds." He downed his drink.

"It's too bad I'm not going straight back to the States," he said, "but I'll see that you get there. Right now I'm heading for Liverpool with a cargo from Bombay. After that, back to the East again.

"But I've good friends in Liverpool, Mister O'Reilly— Soule. We'll work things out when we get there, and keep you safe, too, right under the noses of the English. We'll take one other man into our confidence. My first mate, John Bursley. He's close friends with a Liverpool family that can be trusted to keep you in hiding till we find another ship for you. That sound all right, Mister?"

"It sounds perfect," O'Reilly said. "Somehow I'll find a way to say thank you. Right now I guess I'm too overcome. Nobody could ask for better treatment than I've had on the *Gazelle,* and now I'm finding the same thing on the *Sapphire.*"

"Forget it. We'll have some good long talks between here and the Mersey River." Seiders stood up. "I'd like to entertain you at dinner, Captain, you and Mister Hathaway, but I know you want to get under way, and so do I. I'll go topside now, and have them ready your boat while you say good-by to O'Reilly." He picked up his pipe and strode from the cabin, closing the door behind him.

"John"—Gifford turned to him—"it's been a good voyage, and from the look of things it will be a successful one from here on for all of us. We're going to miss you, though. You've been a good shipmate."

O'Reilly saw Gifford's eyes turn moist, and he knew his own were the same way. Hathaway stood by, unable to say anything.

Gifford reached into his pocket. "You'll need some money when you get to the States, John. We put together what spare cash we had last night—a little over a hundred dollars. Besides that, there's the ten pounds from Father Mac. Here— take it." He held out a roll of bills.

O'Reilly hesitated. "I may never get to America."

Gifford cut him off and put the bills in his hand. "If you never get there, the loss of this money isn't going to matter to any of us. We won't die any the poorer. But you'll get there, John—you'll get there."

O'Reilly turned to Hathaway and put an arm around his shoulders. "Henry, will you do one thing for me?"

"Anything you ask. You know I will."

"Will you keep a log for me, then—starting tonight? I'd hoped to go all the way with the *Gazelle*. But I can't. So will you write the log, and someday in America I'll find you, and then I can read about the rest of the voyage, even if I can't sail it."

Hathaway returned his embrace. "You really love the old ship, don't you?"

"Yes, I do—and every man aboard her. You'd better go now. It'll be dark before you get back."

Later he stood at the rail with Captain Seiders beside him,

and looked across the water to where the lights of the *Gazelle* were shining through the blackness. The *Sapphire* was already under way, her sails taut, straining to round the Cape and reach the open Atlantic before the threatening storm moved in from the west. He stood there listening to the sound of the waves and the rising wind, watching the lights grow fainter and move astern as the distance between the two ships widened. He said nothing, and Captain Seiders understood his silence and did nothing to disturb it.

Gradually the ships drew apart, until they were out of sight of each other.

From the log of Henry Hathaway:

Gazelle, Thursday evening, July 29, 1869—Dear old fellow, I am now seated at the windlass where we've sat side by side for the last five months, more or less, and have been reading over some of your poetry . . . Most everybody on board is talking about you, and they all wish you good luck. All that I have to say is, "Good speed, and God bless you.". . .

Friday evening, July 30—This morning there were six sails in sight, and I suppose the *Sapphire* was one of the six. Much as I would like to have you here, I hope and trust that you are safe where you are. God bless you, old fellow! . . .

Saturday evening, July 31—It is blowing a gale from the westward, and the old ship is lying to under reefed topsail and close-reefed main topsail. . . .

Tuesday evening, August 3—Since this head wind commenced, we have lost about fifty miles of our course, but I think the prospects are good now to get it back again, and perhaps a little more. There are four ships in sight, and if any of them is the *Sapphire* I wish she would come close to us, for I would like to know how you are getting along. I told

Captain Gifford that I felt confident that you are all right with Captain Seiders, as I liked the looks of him the moment I set eyes on him. . . .

Wednesday, August 11—This has been a beautiful day, such a one as you used to like when you were on board. The wind has been very light, but fair. . . . May the Being whose ever-watchful eye is upon us watch over and comfort you in all your troubles. And don't, for Heaven's sake, John (whatever your troubles may be), give up your evening practice. Good night, old boy! God bless you! . . .

Tuesday, November 9—It is my dog watch below, and I have spent most of it playing the flutina and reading over some of your poetry. . . . I hope and pray, old boy, that before this time you have sodded your hoof on Yankee shores. . . . I wish this voyage was over. I haven't had a letter from home for sixteen months. . . .

Saturday, December 18—I often think of you and ask myself if there is any doubt about your safety. . . . With the help of God, I will soon be with you. I hope the time is not far hence when some of your old friends from Australia will be with you, enjoying freedom instead of bondage. . . . May the time soon arrive when they will have a helping hand to assist them in escaping. There goes eight bells. . . .

Wednesday, April 5, 1870—It is my watch below and I have been trying to sleep, but I find it impossible to do so. . . . We have been lying here within a thousand miles of home for the last four or five days, with head winds and calms, but I have no doubt that it is all for the best. The wind is fair now, but quite light, and I expect to be home in a few days. There are three sails in sight, all homeward bound. God speed the plow! Good-by.

21. FREEDOM LANDFALL

THE SAPPHIRE struggled north through the early hours of that August, fighting the same western gale that had forced the *Gazelle* to lay to. She plunged through heavy seas, with her sails close-reefed, barely making headway. The waves were like frothing mountains, and the wind was a steady high scream, and it took the desperate strength of all hands to hold her on her course. O'Reilly stayed in Seiders' cabin for the first few hours, until he heard the timbers and masts of the *Sapphire* straining in the fury of the storm. Then he made his way to the slop chest, and outfitted himself with foul-weather gear, and reported topside to Captain Seiders as an extra hand on deck.

Next day, as quickly as it had struck, the gale blew itself out and moved on. The *Sapphire* seemed almost to shake herself with relief, and then to stretch out for the northward voyage with her sails billowing and her bow cutting sharply through the seas. By that Tuesday evening, as Hathaway had written in his log, the weather had cleared and there were four sails in sight. O'Reilly thought he could recognize one ship in the far distance as the *Gazelle,* but he couldn't be sure. Perhaps it was just a trick of the imagination—just a longing. After a while she had dropped out of sight in the spreading darkness. He wondered if he would ever see her again.

So the days and the weeks went by, and the voyage toward England turned long and restful and lazy.

It was a good free life on the *Sapphire,* but it lacked the thrill of dangerous action. The *Sapphire* followed a trade route, and not the unpredictable route of a wandering whale.

She was speedier than the *Gazelle*, but there was a certain monotony to her course. She never veered from the trade lanes. O'Reilly could go to the chart table at any time, and pick up the dividers and mark off with fair certainty exactly where she'd be on the next day or the next day or the next— a straight chain of dots across the South Atlantic, barring storms and calms.

But the new kind of shipboard life gave O'Reilly spare hours with books and poetry. And there was good companionship, too, with Seiders and Bursley, especially when they sat on deck at night, talking softly in the darkness, planning how to handle the stop-off in Liverpool. It was good companionship, he reflected, but still it was not the active stimulation of the *Gazelle*. But perhaps it was just as well, he told himself; perhaps it was time for a rest, and for long hours of just watching the sea and the sky and trying to trap the heart of a new poem and tell about it on paper.

As the nights wore on, he grew into the habit of standing forward by the rail, watching the phosphorus on the waves for a while, and then the stars above the masts, and smoking and wondering what lay ahead for him. He was standing there one night when it came to him how closely he was following the same path back that the *Hougoumont* had followed on her terrible voyage to Australia. He saw the Southern Cross gradually fading low astern, and the North Star gradually coming over the horizon up ahead, shining higher and brighter each night, and he remembered when he had watched them in just the opposite pattern so many months before. After a time they crossed the equator again, sailing west-northwest, and the nights were hot and the breeze gentle, and it seemed to him once more that he could smell the scent of the ancient African coast being wafted out across the water from somewhere below the horizon, far off to starboard.

And so they moved on, and August became September and September became brisk and changed to October. There were cold gale winds off the Bay of Biscay—gray seas and flying spray and low, speeding clouds. They were nearing port.

They passed the headlands of Cornwall, and he stared at the coast and thought how close he was to the Devon plains and Dartmoor Prison, and the thought made him shiver. They went in from the open sea, past the mouth of Bristol Channel, with Swansea and Cardiff somewhere off to starboard in the fog. And they went slowly past the beautiful shoreline of Milford Haven, and he turned and stared hopelessly into the mist that lay across the sea toward the west, as though his eyes could pierce the cold gray fog and see again the green shores of Ireland.

And then, one early morning, they lay to off the broad mouth of the Mersey, waiting for sunrise and a light westerly breeze to carry them in from the Irish Sea to the crowds and smells of the Liverpool docks.

He was only a few days on English soil again. All that first day, after the *Sapphire* tied up and began discharging her Eastern cargo, they left him hidden in a small locked closet just off Captain Seiders' cabin. There were Englishmen coming and going aboard—agents, port officials, mail handlers, clerks, and merchants—but Seiders had promised him he'd be safe in the hideaway. Apparently there was no reason for anyone to link the name of John Soule with the name of John Boyle O'Reilly, and even if there had been, Seiders assured him, no man would open that door until the last English visitor had gone, no matter how long that might take.

O'Reilly was comfortable in his hideout. He listened to the sounds that came, muffled, from the decks and companionways. A little light seeped in, from a ventilation opening near the overhead. It was enough to read by—and he had room to stretch a bit. It was much more comfortable, he reflected, than the cells at Dartmoor—and certainly less confining than the crockery locker where Hathaway had put him, under the loose step aboard the *Gazelle*. He had books, water, pen and paper. He read for a time and wrote poetry for a time, and sat for a very long time just thinking back over the years and trying to look ahead to those that were coming.

For some reason, this time he was not at all uneasy or frightened. That was strange, he murmured, because he was almost within arm's reach of the British. He could hear their voices clearly most of the time. Yet he felt more secure than he had at Roderique, or even than he had when the *Gazelle* had first sailed foaming from Geographe Bay. Probably it was because there was no reason for anyone to suspect that he was aboard the *Sapphire;* there was no conceivable way for anyone to have traced him. If they were hunting for him at all —and he supposed they would be always—they'd still be watching the course of the *Gazelle*.

He felt in his hip pocket, absently, and touched the bulge that was there. Bursley had given him a pistol, just in case anything went wrong. He took it out and examined it carefully. It was a good weapon, well balanced; it felt easy to handle. He put it back in his pocket with a hope that he would never have to use it. He'd had enough of violence for one lifetime. Still, he felt more secure just from the weight of the weapon and from its firmness against his hip.

He found his thoughts going back to other persons, to those he'd loved. He wondered about his mother, if he'd ever see her grave. Probably not. Probably, too, his brother Will was dead by now, and in some grave he'd never see. Will had never been strong. A few months of British prison life would certainly have sent him to his death.

For the first time in weeks he thought about his aunt Crissy back in Preston, and his uncle James who had taken him by ship from Drogheda, and he remembered how much he had enjoyed living and working in that city—and yet, what a waste the weeks had been, for he'd done nothing constructive. Still, he smiled as he thought of Aunt Crissy. He had been very fond of her. He must remember to tell Seiders and Bursley to visit her sometime when they were on shore.

His thoughts turned to Drogheda again, and then strangely to the little graveyard at Dowth. He remembered the time when he'd been a small boy, and had gone there and selected a flat stone in the wall of the church, and had somehow managed to cut his initials there in the surface—J. B. O'R. He had wanted to be buried just under that spot, he loved Dowth so much. Now probably he'd never see the place again.

Abandoning his memories he took his pen and turned to writing poetry again, pausing from time to time to listen to the sounds from outside—to the creaking of ropes and falls, the sound of Bursley's voice or Seiders', shouting orders. After a while he fell asleep.

It was very late that night when he sat up drowsily at last and listened to the sound of a key rattling in the lock. The door opened then, and Seiders and Bursley came in together. The rest of the ship was silent. "Come along," Seiders said. "We'll take you to a hiding place on shore. They're ready for you now." They wrapped a black cape around him, and led him topside. He saw with thankfulness that it was raining hard, and that it would look perfectly natural for him to walk the streets with the cape pulled high about his face. It was long after midnight, and except for a watchman huddled in the shelter of a shed, there was no one in sight. The night was too stormy and too far gone for any prowlers to be abroad.

They went down the *Sapphire's* slippery gangway, hurrying as anyone would through the rain, Seiders on one side of him and Bursley on the other. They crossed the dock and turned down a cobbled alley. The street lamps cast a feeble dim light on the wet stones. Seiders spoke in hoarse, low tones.

"We've a carriage waiting, two corners away."

"Good!" O'Reilly bent low against the rain, keeping pace with them, saying nothing more. Briefly, he glanced ahead.

Then abruptly he stopped. Barely ten yards off, sheltered in a doorway, he saw a policeman watching them through the wind-blown rain. The man was holding his lantern in one hand and clutching the collar of his uniform coat with the other. He was studying them curiously.

O'Reilly acted on impulse. "Follow me!" he whispered to the others. Then he hurried forward alone, straight to the sheltering doorway, and stepped under the arch and shook the rain from his cape.

"Nasty night," he said to the policeman.

"Aye, it is, sir."

"Maybe you can tell us——"

Seiders and Bursley came hurrying up and stepped under the arch beside him. The policeman held his lantern high and peered at them closely.

"Maybe you can tell us," O'Reilly went on, "how we get to Lime Street from here. I told my captain and his friend here you'd probably know."

"From the Yankee ship, are you?" The policeman waited.

"Yes, that's right."

"I thought as much. You didn't sound English a bit. It's the accent, you know. Well—here's what I'd do, if I were you. Go down to that next street down there and turn left. Then walk two blocks and turn right——"

The policeman went on, giving a complicated set of directions. They listened in silence till he'd finished.

"You've got it now, sir?" he asked.

"We have," O'Reilly said. "Thank you very much. We'll do what you said."

"Good night, sir!"

They pulled their capes high again, and hurried off through the rain. As soon as they'd turned the corner, Seiders stopped.

"That was a damn-fool thing to do!" He burst out laughing. O'Reilly and Bursley were suddenly holding their sides, trying to keep their laughter down.

"Believe me, I'm sorry!" O'Reilly said. "I couldn't help it. There'd never be another chance like that—my first night ashore, and running straight into a bobby. And getting help from him! I'll remember it and be happy about it for years."

Seiders squeezed his arm. "Don't blame you, John. But come on now—the carriage is right around the corner. We'll get you to where you'll be safe."

They hid him in a cellar room in the home of Bursley's friends, and he stayed there for two more days. Then they came for him again in the middle of another rainy night, and again there was a winding ride through the wet Liverpool streets and down to the docks, and once again they hurried him through the cobbled alleys and across the docks, then up a gangplank and onto a strange ship.

She was the bark *Bombay* of Bath, Maine. And her master was sitting in his cabin, waiting for them, with his cigar half-smoked and a Bible on the desk in front of him. He rose when O'Reilly and the others came into the cabin, and he spoke in a loud, deep voice.

"Been expecting you! Jordan's my name." He held out his hand to O'Reilly. "F. C. Jordan of Brunswick—a down-East

Yankee, and I don't like the English. That's why this interests me. Sit down, Mister O'Reilly." He gestured to a chair beside his. Seiders and Bursley took other seats.

Captain Jordan was abrupt, straight to the point.

"I know the whole story," he said. "Captain Seiders here told me everything. Shake hands again, Mister O'Reilly—I like what you're doing and what you stand for. Know why I don't like the English?"

"Why is that?" O'Reilly accepted a cigar.

"I was master of a good ship during the Civil War. Damned good ship she was. I was minding my own business and enjoying the freedom of the seas. Then one day that blasted Anglo-Confederate privateer the *Alabama* crossed my bow, and when she was done with me I was ruined. I owe them something for that. They tell me you're a good sailor, Mister O'Reilly."

"I'd say so, Captain," he replied.

"Very well, then. You're my third mate. The one I had is staying here sick. Might as well hang on to the name of John Soule if anybody asks you before we leave port. But I don't guess they will. We're going out with the morning tide. Come along with me, sir, and I'll show you your quarters. You can freshen up a little. Captain Seiders, you and Mister Bursley stay here, if you will, and we'll be back in a minute and share a farewell drink with you. And I guess Mister O'Reilly'll want to shake hands with you before you go. Come along, sir —it's this way."

Two days out of Liverpool, O'Reilly was sitting in his cabin and putting some of his thoughts into poetry when Captain Jordan sent word for him to come on deck.

Twilight was coming, and the shadows were just beginning to move across the Irish Sea. The water was calm and the air was still and soundless. The *Bombay* was moving along gently and steadily, not making speed but riding on a smooth, straight course.

O'Reilly went to the captain's side, where he was standing against the quarterdeck rail. Jordan smiled at him warmly, and handed him a spyglass and pointed off toward the western horizon.

"Keep your eye there, Mister O'Reilly," he said. "Just beneath the path where the sun's going down. You'll see the coast of Ireland in a moment before the light disappears. Thought you might want to take a last look."

The sun rode low in the sky, but its light shone brightly across the water. O'Reilly raised the glass and focused it in the direction the captain had pointed. He saw thick clouds making up on the horizon. And then, showing clearly through the sunlight, he saw the green hills of Ireland sloping gently to the sea. He stared at the scene for a long time, until it began to fade, and finally disappeared, and then he handed the spyglass back to Captain Jordan again.

"Perhaps the sun is shining on my mother's grave," he said.

Captain Jordan nodded wordlessly.

That night, while off watch in the stillness of his cabin, O'Reilly wrote it down—to remember for the rest of his life:

> Ireland was there, under the sun; but under the dark cloud also. The rays of golden glory fell down from behind the dark cloud—fell down like God's pity on the beautiful tear-stained face of Ireland—fell down on the dear familiar faces of my old home, on the hill, the wood, the river, lighting them all once more with the same heaven-tint that I loved to watch long ago.
>
> Oh, how vividly did that long-ago rise up before me then— the happy home, the merry playmates, the faces, the voices

of dear ones who are there still, and the hallowed words of dearest ones who are dead. Down on all fell the great glory of the setting sun, lighting that holy spot that I might never see, a mother's grave, and lighting the heart with sorrow-shaded devotion.

Home, friends, all that I loved in the world were there, almost beside me—there under the sun—and I, for loving them, a hunted outlawed fugitive, an escaped convict, was sailing away from all I treasured—perhaps forever.

The *Bombay* made a safe and quiet voyage across the North Atlantic. She moved down the East Coast, and then one day she sailed up Delaware Bay, to put in at Philadelphia. O'Reilly stepped ashore on the twenty-third of November. At first he stood as though in a daze, a free man at last, watching other free men move here and there along the crowded water front. It came to him sharply that just two years before, on that same day, he had been sailing south aboard the *Hougoumont,* bound for the swamps and the chains. He put the memory out of his mind quickly. Then he picked up his sea bag, turned once for a quick wave at the *Bombay,* and set off to hunt for the nearest policeman.

He had reached America at last. Now he had a question he wanted to ask: which way should be go to find the United States District Court? A room and a job could come later. First, he wanted to apply for citizenship papers.

IV

SECURITY

(1869–1890)

Great men grow greater by the lapse of time.
  We know the least whom we have seen the latest;
And they, 'mongst those whose names have grown sublime,
  Who worked for Human Liberty, are greatest.
From "A Nation's Test."

22. STRANGER IN THE STREETS

HE STAYED only a short time in Philadelphia. It was a city that failed to stir him; he felt no challenge, no response. He walked its streets, liking it well enough, for it was the first city he had known as a free man since his days in Dublin. But liking a place was not enough; there was too much work to be done. He sat in the parks for a while, thinking how pleasant it was not to have to run and hide any more—and at the same time, how unpleasant to have no field of action. There was a lot that he wanted to say and do; he knew that in some vague way, but he wasn't completely sure of how to go about it, or even of what it was. At any rate, he sensed that Philadelphia was not the place to begin.

He had money enough to keep eating and to keep out of the rain for a while. From the day he'd gone aboard the *Gazelle*, it seemed that nobody had let him spend anything. So he had the money that Father Mac had passed along to Captain Gifford, and the money that Gifford and Hathaway had collected for him on the *Gazelle*. Also, Captain Seiders on the *Sapphire* and Captain Jordan on the *Bombay* each had paid him a mate's wages for the help he'd given aboard ship. So, for the moment, he wasn't worried about getting along.

But he was beginning to worry about the future after only three or four days ashore. After all he'd been through for the past three years, it seemed senseless—almost sinful—to waste his new freedom sitting in the parks and enjoying the autumn winds and paying visits to Independence Hall. Yet, there seemed no way to get started on anything constructive, no first step on which to place his feet.

And so he walked back to the water front one day, to see if the *Bombay* was still in port. He did it on the chance that somebody—though he couldn't imagine who—might be trying to get in touch with him through the ship. She was still there, almost ready for sea again, taking on the last pieces of cargo for the run back across the Atlantic to Liverpool. He stood off and looked at her with affection. For a moment he was tempted to ask for his mate's berth back again; but then the thought of always having to hide and run drove the idea quickly from his mind.

He had guessed right. There was a message aboard for him, sent by a group of local Fenians, giving the address of their meeting place and asking him to visit them as soon as he could. Their agents in England, they said, had sent word of his crossing on the *Bombay*. It startled him a little, to realize that the news had crossed as quickly as the ship.

He went to their meeting place, in the dirty back room of a warehouse, where a few men sat arguing in thick cigar smoke and—it seemed to him—did far more complaining than planning. The whole thing depressed him and irritated him, including the way they questioned him. They might have used the same attitude after catching an impostor or criminal red-handed. They seemed incredulous, suspicious, hostile.

"You're Boyle O'Reilly—from the *Bombay?*"

"Yes."

"Boyle O'Reilly the poet?"

"Yes."

"The man that got away from Australia?"

"Yes."

"But you're young—you're quiet. How do we know you're the right Boyle O'Reilly?" They questioned him as though he were a witness under cross-examination.

O'Reilly stood it for a while, and then felt that if he listened to much more he'd lose his temper and wind up in a fight. He'd be glad to get away from the dirty room anyhow; this wasn't Fenianism as he remembered it. He stood up to leave.

"Gentlemen, I didn't come looking for you. You came looking for me. I didn't come here to ask any favor—I came at your request. I've answered your questions. If you think I'm a liar, I can't help it. But I'm under no obligation to stay here and be questioned any more. I'll leave now, before we have trouble."

That changed the whole atmosphere.

"One moment," they said. "We're sorry. We had to be sure. Can you wait just a moment, and tell us your plans?"

"I don't see how it's any business of yours," O'Reilly said, "but my plans are to leave Philadelphia at once. There's no field for me here—no friends—none of the opportunities I'd hoped to find in America. I'll try some other city."

"New York, perhaps?"

"Perhaps. Why?"

They handed him a piece of paper with writing on it. "Will you look up John Savage at this address?—it's the Fenian headquarters in New York. He wants a good speaker for a meeting at Cooper Institute on the sixteenth. You should be a good speaker."

O'Reilly took it with a shrug, and headed out of Philadelphia that same day. At least it was a start. At least it was something that might lead to something else. And it did. His reception in New York was as enthusiastic as his stay in Philadelphia had been depressing. And for a time he was dazed by its warmth and sincerity.

On the night of December 16 he stood on the platform at Cooper Institute and the tears came to his eyes as two thousand people cheered his name. He wondered if he deserved it. He wondered why they should care so much. Behind him sat Savage, presiding at the meeting. On either side of the chairman were other Fenian leaders, standing up to applaud and shout. Before him, as Savage and the others rose, the whole audience got to its feet in a wave of loud cheers. Still he wondered why.

And after a while, standing there, he understood. This was the heart of Fenianism in America. Philadelphia had been just an offshoot, drained of money and energy. But here in New York were thousands of Irish who had become Americans, and who were determined to keep a corner of their hearts apart for the people back home—the people who were struggling against oppression in the cities and villages, in the churches and the public houses.

To them, he realized now, he was a living symbol. He was proof, standing before them, that a man could break the British chains and escape to freedom, and could still carry with him the flaming spirit that had first brought about his sufferings.

He gave a moving talk that night—a talk of the never-ending fight for Irish freedom, of the sacrifices of men such as Chambers and McCarthy and his own brother Will, of the horrors of the prisons, of the constant Fenian penetrations into the ranks of the British Army. And he told also of the sympathy and good will he had found among the Americans on the ships, among the crews and officers of the *Gazelle* and the *Sapphire* and the *Bombay*. He told them how glad he was to have reached their country. The meeting was a tremendous success. He sensed just what the crowd was longing to hear, to bolster its spirits and optimism. And he gave it to them from the heart, knowing that those who listened and cheered would write letters about it to friends and relatives back in Ireland, and in turn keep up the spirits in that land.

It was a great evening. Still, New York was not for him either. He felt that as strongly as he had felt that Philadelphia was wrong for him. And a few nights later he talked about it with Savage, sitting in a water-front alehouse and listening to the sound of the wind moaning in from the Hudson River.

"What can I do?" He spread his hands helplessly. "I want to help Ireland, but even more than that, I want to help all men to live together like brothers. That's the way it was written for them to live when this country began. There must be some way I can do both of those things at the same time— help Ireland and help all men. But while I'm doing it, I'll have to buy bread. What can I do? Where can I begin?"

Savage nodded. He sipped his drink before he spoke. "You've been a newspaperman—a soldier—a poet—a sailor."

"And a convict courier, a mahogany sawyer, and a whale-boat man," O'Reilly said. "There may be vacancies for men like that these days, but I've had enough."

"And you're a good public speaker," Savage went on. "Let's remember newspapers, poetry, and public speaking— and forget the rest. Now, how do we use you in those fields?"

"On a newspaper, obviously," said O'Reilly. "If I can make a name for myself on a paper—work hard and make a real name—the poetry and the public speaking will follow. And then I can get across the message of tolerance and the message of the rights of man. I've thought of all that, naturally."

Savage called for another round of ale. "Don't try it in New York," he advised. "It's easier to make your voice heard in some other city. And there's only one city I know of that would fully understand what you'd be saying, and would up-hold your right to say it. That's Boston."

O'Reilly's eyes came to life. "I'd wondered about that. I'd like to try it there. How would I begin?"

"That'll be taken care of," Savage told him. "I'll get letters of introduction for you—to Thomas Manning and Dr. Richard Dwyer Joyce. They're cultured gentlemen—men of some influence—and they think the same way you do. Yes, Boston will be the best place for you. And the Boston *Pilot* would be the best paper for you to try. It's owned by a man named Patrick Donahoe. You'll like him. His home was in County Cavan. He sailed to Boston forty-five years ago, started the *Pilot* in 1836. Now he's the wealthiest Irishman in New England. The *Pilot* is a weekly, with a powerful voice, and it's been supporting the Irish-American-Catholic cause since the first day it went to press. Yes, O'Reilly, that's where we're going to send you. Let's drink to it."

The next few days seemed to O'Reilly to drag without end. He wandered around New York while waiting for Savage to come to him with the letters of introduction. He studied a variety of American newspapers to get acquainted with their styles and principles. He went for long walks, along the cold water front and through the parks and the business districts. He spent a lonely Christmas by himself, listening to the songs of wandering carol groups and watching children out for a winter's walk in their bright warm clothes. And he walked to other parts of the city, and saw other children trudging to work on Christmas Day, their hands red with the cold and their legs wrapped in old rags. There was a lot to be done in this country, too, he reflected. It wasn't all freedom and light and happiness, not by far. He went deeper into the slums, and saw men huddled asleep in open doorways and in alley corners, with their faces showing the lines of defeat and hopelessness and moral breakdown. He felt sorry for them, and for their lost dreams, and he knew it was kinder to go walking by without disturbing them.

Finally, one day Savage brought the letters. O'Reilly left

New York that same morning. And he arrived in Boston on the second day of 1870.

They welcomed him with undisguised pleasure. They made room for him in the Manning home, and they brought in a young lawyer named Patrick A. Collins and introduced him as the future mayor of Boston. They called in Dr. Joyce, with a reminder to bring along some of his poetry. And they talked about O'Reilly's problem, and urged him not to waste himself as a public lecturer with a limited audience, and certainly not to throw away his talents on politics. It had to be on a newspaper, they said—that's where O'Reilly would have to find his outlet. And the *Pilot* was the place to start. They'd fix that up with Donahoe as soon as they had the chance; and meanwhile, there was a job waiting for him as a clerk with the Inman Steamship Company. The Boston manager was an Irishman named Merrick S. Creagh, and was a good friend of both Collins and Joyce. He could report for work in the morning.

O'Reilly was eager to get started with the *Pilot,* but meanwhile he did as his new friends advised him. He reported for work, and stuck to his job with the Inman company, and went off on a long round of speaking engagements that were lined up for him by Manning, Joyce, and Collins.

"We've got to make you known, John," they told him. "Don't worry about the money. Move around and get known."

He lectured in Boston's Music Hall the night of January 31 before a big audience. His topic was "England's Political Prisoners." The applause was even better than at Cooper Institute. At first it startled O'Reilly, then delighted him. By the next morning his name was being talked about in circles that kept widening across Boston.

He went off from time to time to give other lectures—in

Salem, Lawrence, Quincy, Providence—wherever an Irish audience could be brought together. And before long his name was being heard in political and literary groups all through southern New England. The plan was beginning to work.

He refused to accept any pay for his talks. Checks came to him in the mail, and he returned them. "Send them to Ireland," he wrote back. "That's where the money is needed."

He seemed headed for an early success as a brilliant young orator.

Then, suddenly, his own income was snatched away. Somehow, word had crossed the Atlantic to the Inman offices in England that John Boyle O'Reilly—the hunted absconder—was on the company pay roll in Boston. That caused an uproar.

Merrick Creagh got sharp and immediate orders to fire the man or get out himself. They gave him no choice; O'Reilly was out.

For a moment the loss of the job was a shock.

But that night he learned in the Manning home that suddenly it didn't matter. The place O'Reilly had waited for on the *Pilot* was now open and waiting for him. He was to be a reporter, and also an editorial writer.

The new chapter—and the most important one—had begun.

23. BORDER BATTLES

FROM THE TIME he'd first arrived in America, Boyle O'Reilly had kept in touch with his aunt Crissy back in Preston. He'd felt an affection there that had stayed constant through the years they'd been separated. He'd told stories about Aunt Crissy on the *Gazelle* and the *Sapphire* and the *Bombay* and he had urged all his shipmates to stop in and pay her a visit, if ever they happened to be in that part of England. Some of them did.

Whenever he'd had the chance, he had sent her a letter. Her replies—sometimes long in reaching him—had kept him informed on family matters, on the health of his cousin Willy and his uncle James. He wrote her again from Boston, shortly after joining the *Pilot:*

Franklin Street, Boston
April 5, 1870

My own Dear Aunt:

How happy I was made by seeing your letter. I am truly glad that you and Willy and Uncle are so well. I was thinking of you when I was in Liverpool. . . .

I am a very fortunate fellow to pull clear through. I am likely to become a prosperous man in America. I write for the magazines and report for the *Pilot,* drill the Irish Legion, make speeches at public meetings, lecture for charities, etc., etc. This course in the old countries would soon make a fortune, and after a time here it will have the same effect; but at present, all this must be done to establish a reputation. I just manage to live as a gentleman. I have paid my debts to the captains who brought me here. In a few years it will be my own fault if I do not make a name worth bearing. . . .

He had wanted to go on with the letter—to tell her of the beauties of Boston, of the hills that surrounded it, of the broad water front and the great ships that came and went, of the red and black chimneypots and the gabled roofs against a sunset sky. He wanted to write of the warm friendliness of Boston's people, of their love of conversation, and the long hours spent in parlors and taverns alike, arguing about poetry and philosophy and morals. He wanted to write, too, about the countryside around the city, so rich in American history —the old stagecoach trails, the bridge at Concord, the village green at Lexington. He wanted to write of the vigor of big business, in the countinghouses and banks, among the rising stores, along the narrow streets that once were the cowpaths of colonists and now were the avenues of trade.

He wanted to write that, but much of it he knew would be lost to his aunt, until he could take the time to know the city better and write a careful and intimate description of it. And besides, there was work of his own to be done, work in his new role of newspaper reporter and editorial writer. There was no time now for long letters.

It sounded incredible, but around the newspaper rooms there were reports of a Fenian army in the making, getting ready to attack Canada from Vermont. And Boyle O'Reilly had been given the assignment of digging out the facts and— if it were true—of covering the story as the *Pilot's* war correspondent. So he put away his notes to Aunt Crissy, and got quickly to work.

The rumors turned out to be true. He learned that much when he went at night to the old Sherman House to cover a Fenian recruiting rally. And he discovered that the campaign that was about to begin was based on one that had been tried four years earlier. At that time, back in 1866, he learned that General John O'Neill had crossed from Ireland and organized an Irish army of Civil War veterans. His plan had been to strike at England through its distant back door of Canada. And so, with a hardened force of Irishmen and adventurers, he had launched his first raid across the Canadian border from a base near Buffalo.

O'Reilly learned to his surprise that the raid had been successful—up to a point. O'Neill and his troops had captured their objective and had been rocking the Canadian militia back on its heels, when the United States had decided to step in before a real war could get rolling. The Government had sent General Grant north with a fast-moving American force, to cut off O'Neill's line of supplies and reinforcements. The stranded Irish had withdrawn from Canada, with a promise to be back someday and try it again. This, then, was to be the second try. O'Neill was back in command. He confided his strategy to O'Reilly at the Sherman House meeting. His plan was to invade Canada through St. Albans, Vermont.

O'Reilly brought back all that information to the *Pilot,* and was told to go with the invading army and cover the story from the front. For O'Reilly, it was a good assignment. For O'Neill and his army, the raid was a fiasco. Almost nothing went right. O'Reilly watched with sympathy and disgust and told himself that if this was American Fenianism in action, it was slated for a short, unhappy life.

As he wrote of it on May 28, in his opening story to the *Pilot,* it appeared to be a case of the bright and bold courage of a few men betrayed by the ignorance, cowardice, and indifference of many others.

> Your reporter [he wrote] left Boston on Tuesday for St. Albans, Vt., and having provided himself with the morning papers had his imagination inflated to extreme tightness before his second cigar was finished.
>
> Each paper had distinct and detailed accounts of thou-

sands of men and trains of war material. So precise were they in their statements, that even the officers commanding were named.

These statements were all false. There were no thousands of men moving on St. Albans, nor on any other point.

I arrived in St. Albans at six o'clock in the morning. There were about 60 Fenians on the train—40 from Boston under command of Major Hugh McGuinness, and about 20 who were taken on at the various stations.

When the train arrived at St. Albans, these men passed quietly through the town and proceeded to the front beyond Franklin, 17 miles beyond St. Albans.

Along the road between St. Albans and Franklin were scattered groups of men, principally hurrying to the front, but some even at that early stage turning their faces and steps homeward, excusing their cowardice by tales of mismanagement and discontent. However, these dispirited ones grew fewer as we went on, and the hurrying men seemed to lose their weariness as they neared the front.

About ten o'clock we arrived in the village of Franklin. We found the solitary street filled with wagons and teams of every description, and a large crowd of men, composed principally of citizens, attracted by curiosity.

For the first time we saw the uniformed Fenians here in very considerable numbers. The uniform was a capital one for service, and in mass most attractive—a green cavalry jacket, faced with yellow, army blue pantaloons and a blue cap with green band.

General O'Neill commanded in person. He walked up and down the road conversing with his chief of staff, Gen. J. J. Donnelly, observing the occupation of the men, and now and then making some remark to aid a waverer in his choice of two rifles with perhaps equally bright barrels.

Gen. O'Neill was dressed in a light gray suit, and wore a staff sword and spurs. His horse, a small bay, stood by the roadside, held by a green-coated orderly.

When informed of the arrival of a United States Marshal, the General merely smiled and continued his walk. He said to your reporter that he meant to fight, regardless.

Among the officers present was Major Daniel Murphy of Bridgeport, Conn., in command of a very fine body of men. Major Murphy had his men formed up on the road, and minutely inspected them to see if every man's equipment was complete. He looked a fine, soldierly fellow, and throughout the whole day, and since then, no officer or man deserves higher notice than he for conspicuous bravery or clearheaded projects.

Capt. Wm. Cronan of Burlington, Vt., also commanded a splendid company, in perfect uniform and equipment. His men had asked to be given the front in the advance on the enemy, and their request was granted. They were in line farther on the road, going through their manual and platoon drills, and showing by their motions that they were well-disciplined soldiers.

Another company, under the command of Capt. J. J. Monahan, was still nearer the Canadian front. Col. Humphrey Sullivan of Boston; Col. Brown, of Lawrence, Mass.; Major Charles Carlton of Burlington, Vt.; Capt. John Fitzpatrick of Bridgeport, Conn.; Capt. Carey of Fort Edward, and many others were also present.

Of the above-named officers, the name of Capt. John Fitzpatrick should be especially mentioned for personal bravery, shown in the course of the day.

General O'Neill told your reporter that he knew that the Canadians had taken up a position and were prepared for him in force. He said he meant to draw their fire, and find their strength and position—and then he would know whether a project he entertained was feasible or not.

It was not.

An hour before noon U. S. Marshal George P. Foster galloped hurriedly into the encampment and warned O'Neill that he was breaking the federal law. He ordered the general to call off the whole affair. O'Neill ignored him. By way of reply, the general jumped on his bay horse, ordered his troops to fall in with fixed bayonets, rode to the head of the column, and promptly led his army off down a narrow hilly road toward the Canadian line. O'Reilly had borrowed a horse earlier. Now he swung into the saddle and took off after O'Neill. The Canadian line was a mile away, just beyond the brow of a hill and along a small brook.

But Marshal Foster was determined somehow—if he could —to stop the fighting before it broke out. When O'Neill rebuffed him, he galloped on ahead of the advancing Fenians, crested the hill, and hurried down to check on the Canadians and their readiness to fight. He found them on guard and waiting only for the sight of the first Fenian before opening fire.

Back he galloped then, back over the brow of the hill, to make another effort to stop the Irishmen. O'Reilly, riding near the head of the column, saw him wheel alongside O'Neill and heard him shout an excited warning.

"For God's sake, General, be sensible and halt this army! Don't make me have to arrest you! Listen—the Canadians are strung out at the base of the hill there—on that other slope that rises just beyond Alvah Richards' farmhouse. They're in perfect position to open up the instant you move into sight."

To O'Reilly's amazement, the warning drew an immediate cheer from those who heard it. Word of the situation flashed down the column from man to man. The troops flung down their knapsacks and coats, eager for a battle.

Again O'Neill ignored the marshal. He turned in his saddle and beckoned to O'Reilly. "You're a trained soldier," he said, when O'Reilly reached his side. "What do you think of this plan? As soon as we top the hill, I'll send Carey's company and Cronan's down the road as skirmishers. They'll deploy at the base to draw fire—charge the brook if they can. That will give away the Canadians' position. The rest of my men will be under cover. When we see how the Canadians stand, we'll turn their right flank and advance. Our objective is Cook's Corners—two miles to the west. What do you think of it?"

O'Reilly stared at him, astonished. From what the marshal had just said, the plan could become nothing but mass suicide. But O'Neill hadn't waited for an answer. Already he was shouting orders to Cronan and Carey to move their companies forward. O'Reilly saw Colonel Brown, who had no command of his own, grab a breech-loading rifle and hurry off in the wake of Cronan's men.

O'Reilly shrugged helplessly and spurred his horse toward the brow of the hill, to watch the battle develop. It was a brutal shame, he told himself, that men with spirit and fire and courage should be thrown away on anything as fantastic and hopeless as this.

It turned out exactly as he had expected. The Canadians held their fire until the skirmishers were well down the hill and charging the brook with a wild cheer. Then, before Cronan and Carey could deploy their men, a tremendous thunder of gunfire burst from the Canadians in their hidden position. The Fenians were caught in the open.

They fired back blindly. Great gaps opened in their ranks. Dead and wounded fell by the roadside and the bullets blazed back and forth above their bodies.

The Fenians tried to fall back to the Richards house, shouting above the sound of battle for reserves. Send reserves! They got only fifty men, with Generally Donnelly commanding them.

The Canadians raised their sights then, and poured heavy

fire into the main body of O'Neill's troops. O'Neill rallied his men and led them in a fighting rush down the hillside, trying to storm up the opposite slope and force the Canadians out of their line. There was no longer any hope of turning a flank. Now it was nothing but a stand-up, gun-to-gun battle. But with all their courage, men such as Murphy and Sullivan and Fitzpatrick couldn't get the Fenians to advance under the merciless fire from the Canadian slope.

And small wonder, O'Reilly thought, watching them. Even if they got there, they'd be too weak to hold their gains.

Finally, even O'Neill had taken all he could stand. He ordered his men to retreat, and they fell back stubbornly, still shooting at Canadians they couldn't even see, and still with Canadian bullets hitting the ground at their feet.

General Donnelly, with his handful of reserves, stayed in position at the Richards house. The rest of the army fell back until they were past the brow of the hill again. O'Neill in time got there safely, but only to find Marshal Foster waiting with a warrant.

"I warned you, General. Now you've forced me to act. I'm placing you under arrest."

O'Neill sighed, looked around wearily, and saw O'Reilly riding up and taking in the situation.

"Mr. O'Reilly," he said, "you're a general now. I'm turning over my command to you."

O'Reilly sat in his saddle, stunned by the announcement. He started to protest. But before he could say anything, Foster broke in.

"Then I arrest you, too, General O'Reilly. This warrant's broad enough to cover both of you—and a lot more generals besides."

That night, back at St. Albans, O'Reilly telegraphed a dispatch to the *Pilot* that left the staff completely bewildered:

"I have just been arrested by the United States marshal."

He was freed on the next day, however, in time to cover the sorry ending of the story.

That day the Fenians set up a distracting fire from their lone piece of artillery, just long enough to let General Donnelly and his survivors leave the shelter of the Richards house and fall back to rejoin the rest of the army.

They left their Franklin base, then, and moved out across the countryside, heading for the New York state line and the town of Malone. Before long they joined forces near Trout River with another four hundred Fenian soldiers who were just arriving from the south. With their numbers thus swelled, they formed a strong skirmish line and made one more attack on the Canadians, but again they were driven back under heavy fire. This time the Canadians followed their retreat to the international line, captured three prisoners, wounded two men, and then retired to a safe distance on their own soil.

> Your reporter is sorry to have to write it [O'Reilly's story went], but that is what the Fenian officers—not the men— call "the *fight* at Trout River."
>
> As soon as that direful strife was over, "Generals" Starr, O'Leary, and several other generals (we use the word *general* as a mean—there might have been a Colonel, and there probably was a Field Marshal) ordered their carriages, which like prudent soldiers they had kept in readiness in case of failure. They left the men to look after themselves and started for Malone.
>
> There they held a council of war—a favorite occupation of Fenian officers, it would seem.
>
> A great Bashaw of their organization (and of course a General) named Gleason, was here and holding a court at the Ferguson House. He vociferously expressed his "disgust" with affairs in general, and interlarded said expression

with Munchausen assertions of what could be done, were things to his way of thinking, and especially of what he himself could do.

Along the road from Malone to Trout River, the poor disheartened fellows came straggling. Unlike the men at Richards' farm, they had kept their rifles and equipment and notwithstanding the intense heat of the day, great numbers of them still carried their knapsacks and greatcoats. When they gathered in large groups, they imitated their officers so far as to express open disgust, and especially were they disgusted with the man of the Munchausen proclivities.

Your reporter drove out to Trout River, where the encampment had been formed. An immense quantity of military stores was piled there awaiting the men who were *not* coming. Hundreds of young men grouped around in utter disorder. There was very little noise or bustle for so large a gathering, and when the voices of the men were heard in passing through their camp, their tenor was an emphatic and stern condemnation of their officers.

Many of the men, in describing the events to your reporter, burst into tears at what they termed their disgrace, and said they only wanted a man to lead them and they would go anywhere with him.

Judging from the military physique of the greater number, there can be no doubt that with qualified officers these men would prove they did not merit the name they now feared—cowards.

On the following day—with still no leader taking charge —the army began to break up. The depots suddenly were crowded with men trying to board the trains and get away. Others merely picked up their packs, shouldered their gear, and started out on the long, dusty walk that in time would get them home.

O'Reilly returned to Boston. He felt grateful to the United

States Government for stepping in at just the right moment and arresting General O'Neill. Otherwise, the whole affair probably would have become a disgraceful farce even more tragic than it had been. He felt sorry for the men—misled, mishandled, and finally disillusioned. He wondered why that sort of thing happened so often to Irish people, and how they could keep their pride and their courage in the face of its happening. He hoped that his next big assignment for the *Pilot* would find the Irish-Americans in a happier role.

But it didn't work out that way.

24. IRISH AGAINST IRISH

O'REILLY WAS about to learn that the immigrant Irishman in America, for the most part, remained as wholly Irish at heart as his grandfather had been. He remained a transplant, unchanged in any way except for the soil underfoot. If he contemplated any changes, he was content to let them wait until the next generation came along, when Americanism might begin to dominate Irish nationalism. He was not interested in accepting changes before that happened.

Meanwhile, the Irishman in America cherished and nourished and clung to the same emotional urgings that had been his grandfather's back at the crossroads. It seemed that nobody had ever presented a good argument for acting otherwise. But Boyle O'Reilly came up with one, in a burst of shock and shame and anger.

It was July 12, a significant day on the calendar of Protestant Ireland. It was the day for remembering the anniversary of the Battle of the Boyne. Thousands of Orangemen gathered for a big Protestant parade in New York. They milled around, grabbing flags and banners, anti-Catholic posters with painted insults, sticks and clubs for the street fights they knew would be coming. They whipped themselves into crazy enthusiasm with music and shouts and jeers. Finally, they formed into line and began their march. They pounded along the pavements to the rhythm of their own wild chant:

"To hell with the Pope!—To hell with the Pope!—To hell with the Pope!"

A battle of some sort was inevitable. Catholics along the

line of march heard the chant and quickly formed forces. They took up clubs and stones, and raced to Elm Park, where the celebration was supposed to have its climax. The front of the parade marched into the park. A pistol shot rang out. The fight was on; and when it was over four Irishmen lay dead in the streets and scores more were injured.

Probably not one man on the scene that day could look back on a record as completely and loyally Irish as O'Reilly's —a record of being born on the banks of the Boyne, of staking his life for his country, of suffering the brutal and degrading tortures of Dartmoor and of the whole British penal code, and of turning deliberately to America as a means of aiding Ireland—not of aiding himself.

Yet his reaction of mixed shame and disgust at the New York riot did not distinguish between Catholic and Protestant, between Fenian and Orangeman. They were Irishmen, that was all that counted. They were Irishmen disgracing Ireland before the world, and in a sense insulting the country that had taken them in by throwing their own dirt in its face.

He wrote his feelings in a *Pilot* editorial for any Irishman to read regardless of loyalties:

> Events have at intervals occurred in the history of this country which have justly called up a blush of shame on the faces of patriotic Irishmen. But we doubt if they ever received so great a reason for deep humiliation as during the past week.
>
> On the 12th of July the American Protestant Association —in other words, the Orange Lodges of New York—had advertised their intention of celebrating the anniversary of the Battle of the Boyne. Accordingly on that morning, with colors flying and bands playing, they paraded to the number of 3,000 and marched to the scene of their celebration, Elm Park.

On the line of march they lost no opportunity of goading to intensity the bitter feelings of their Catholic fellow-countrymen whom they passed. This resulted in a general banding of the laborers of the vicinity, who set upon the Orangemen with sticks and stones, which were answered by them with pistol bullets. A terrible melee was the consequence, in which four lives were lost and numbers endangered.

Is not this cause for deep humiliation?

Earnest men have labored for years to remove that bitter old taunt of our enemies—"You cannot unite." Patient workers have tried to teach the world, and even ourselves, that this reproach was not the truth. This is the reward of their labor. Our own people, in a strange land, have insultingly turned on their benefactors and flung their labor in their faces.

Oh, what a national degradation is this! *We* talk of patriotism and independence! *We* prate and boast of our "national will"! What evidence is this? What are we today in the eyes of Americans? Aliens from a petty island in the Atlantic, boasting of our patriotism and fraternity, and showing at the same moment the deadly hatred that rankles against our brethren and fellow-countrymen.

Why must we carry, wherever we go, these accursed and contemptible island feuds? Shall we never be shamed into the knowledge of the brazen impudence of allowing our national hatreds to disturb the peace and safety of the respectable citizens of this country? Must the day come when the degrading truth cannot be muffled up, that the murderous animosity of Irish partyism has become a public nuisance in almost every corner of the world?

We cannot dwell on this subject. We cannot, and we care not to analyze this mountain of disgrace, to find out to which party the blame is attached. Both parties are to be blamed and condemned, for both have joined in making the name of Irishman a scoff and a by-word this day in America.

He sent the editorial to be printed, grateful that he'd had
the opportunity of writing it. There was a real mission to be
accomplished here. He could see it plainly now. He could
help Ireland by trying to help the Irish forget their internal
enmities—help them to become one people, with the single
goal of Irish independence. He had the voice and the mouth-
piece, and the freedom to use both. He made a special visit
to church that day, and thanked God for guiding him to
America and to Boston and to the *Pilot,* where he could speak
out as he liked.

The editorial hit like a thunderclap. Irishmen read it in
Boston, in New York, in Philadelphia. They read it a second
time, wondering if they could believe what they saw; and
then they passed it along for others to read. This was something new—an Irishman speaking from a plane above partyism!

Some read the piece and applauded it. Most who read it
condemned it. The average loyal Orangeman swore he wasn't
going to burn his colored ribbon overnight. The average
loyal Irish Catholic swore he wasn't going to refrain from
grabbing up a club when somebody shouted "To hell with
the Pope!" But whether they liked it or recoiled from it,
thousands of Irishmen read the piece. That was all that mattered for the moment to Boyle O'Reilly—that he had found
both an outlet and an audience, and that he might have
started one or two Irishmen thinking along constructive
lines.

But he knew—and he said as much to Manning and Joyce
and Collins that night—that neither this nor a thousand
editorials could change in a few weeks what had been built
and shaped over the passing of centuries.

"Next year," he said, "they'll be at it again. They'll do the
same things. And the Irish-American press will be pouring

oil on the flames—feeding the fury. So next year I'll write it
again—and for as many years as I have the chance. And
maybe someday, if enough of us keep writing it and saying it,
we'll make them understand."

He was right about the next year. The Orangemen paraded
again in New York. Pistols were fired, bricks were hurled,
clubs were swung, and skulls were cracked. That time
O'Reilly tried to make his editorial approach both temperate
and analytical. Perhaps, if he appealed to their reason, he
could make them see the error.

> On both sides of the question [he wrote] there have been
> made about enough wild and intemperate assertions, charges
> and countercharges. . . .
> Certain it is that the Orange procession is not a pleasant
> sight to *any* Irish Catholic, however unprejudiced. But it is
> just as certain that the Irish Catholics of this country, as a
> body, condemn all breach of the law in attacking an Orange
> procession, just as honestly as they would condemn a riot of
> any other criminal nature.
> There are two ways of getting rid of this apple of dis-
> cord.
> The first is, by an agreement between the general Irish
> population and the Orangemen, foregoing all right to pa-
> rade and expressing their determination never to hold pro-
> cessions for Irish political objectives alone. This, we may rest
> assured, will not be easily agreed to.
> The second way is the better, and the one that must come
> in the end—when America, tired out and indignant with
> her squabbling population, puts her foot down with a
> will and tells them all—Germans, French, Irish, Orange—
> "You have had enough now. There is only ONE flag to be
> raised in the future in this country and that flag is the Stars
> and Stripes."

The editorial startled Irishmen, Orangemen, and native-
born Americans alike. It was the sound of a strong new voice,

crying a strong doctrine, and yet a doctrine that was as old as the nation itself.

O'Reilly sat back at his desk in the *Pilot* office and waited for the reaction to explode over his head. He knew it was coming, and he welcomed it. This, he'd decided, was the way he was going to talk for as many years as God granted him to live in America, and it was best to find out directly at the beginning just how his audience was going to line up and how broadly it might expand.

Then the letters came pouring in, and the editorials in other newspapers joined the rising chorus of comment. He was praised for being honest, rebuked for being dishonest. He was the spirit of loyalty, the spirit of treachery. He was a hot-headed Harp, he was a clear-thinking diplomat. He was a bumbling fool who didn't understand the issues, and a brilliant leader who cut swiftly to the very heart of great problems. It was precisely the sort of comment he had hoped to arouse. He was delighted.

He chose one letter, printed in the *Pilot,* as the peg on which to hang his answer to all the praise and criticism.

> On our third page [he wrote] will be found a letter signed "Corcoran" purporting to be an expression of Fenian dissatisfaction with our editorial on the New York riot.
>
> When we wrote that editorial we were fully aware that it would not be acceptable to certain people in the community. But we know that therein we expressed the opinions of the calm, rational, and respectable Irish Catholics of America. Least of all did we expect dissatisfaction from the Fenians, whose temperate action in New York, during the excitement immediately preceding the riot, won for them the well-merited praise of every class in the community.
>
> We must, as a friend, remind the writer of this letter that his assertion that we "sneer at the Sunburst" is extremely unjust—and he knows it. Boasting is not our trade, but none of them all loves the Sunburst better than we do.

The writer also says, "The *Pilot* has entirely changed its tone on Fenianism, and, from being friendly, adopted directly the opposite course."

The *Pilot* has done no such thing. The *Pilot* is as true a friend to all organizations aiming at Ireland's good, now, as it ever has been, and ever shall be. Still, we must reserve our right to criticize unfavorably as well as the opposite.

It is said that "There has been no change in the circumstances of Ireland, nor in the principles or policy of the Fenian Brotherhood," but that all the change has been in ourselves.

That is incorrect. There has been a very great change in the circumstances of Ireland since the Fenian Brotherhood was a great organization, and, whether in its policy or not, there has been a vast change in the organization.

We don't believe in that ignorant old prejudice that sneers at every man who changes his opinions. There is much of Ireland's bane in the habit. The man who has the courage to honestly change his opinions is the best man.

If convinced that we were pursuing a wrong course, or that a better one was open, we would change every day in the year. The world is all change. Every thinker is a changer —every discovery is a change. Only an ignorant or thoughtless person can believe that a man who changes is a bad man. Such a belief would sink the world in stagnation in a day.

Our friends may rest assured that, with God's assistance, we shall never change from the Right or turn our back on the Truth. But in all debatable questions our motto is— "It is better to be Right than Stubborn!"

25. AT ANCHOR

THOSE EARLY MONTHS of his career in Boston gave Boyle
O'Reilly something he always had dreamed of having
—a life that was part Bohemian and part hard work.
He enjoyed the easy freedom of a bachelor's career. He enjoyed the challenge of becoming part of a fast-growing city.

His room was on the top floor of a lodging house in Staniford Street, near Boston's West End. It was in a location that
caught the salt freshness of the east wind as it moved in from
the open Atlantic and past the islands and across the crowded
harbor, breaking the heat in the summer and melting the
snow in the winter.

The room was within easy walking distance of the places
that first began to attract O'Reilly—Bunker Hill in Charlestown or Faneuil Hall or the Old North Church in the North
End for historic pilgrimages; the Parker House for lobster or
Marliave's for spaghetti or Billy Parks' Tavern for ale and
roast beef; the long water front with its spiderwebs of spars
and rigging and jutting bowsprits and its tarry smell; Boston
Common with its quiet walks and its tall trees; and always
the *Pilot,* for work that went on many times until the late
hours of night—work that soon began drawing notice and
comment from all parts of the country.

His Staniford Street room became a meeting place for a
group of male friends that kept growing bigger, until frequently it had to adjourn to a nearby alehouse. Into the circle
came the men he had met first in Boston—Manning, Dr.
Joyce, Patrick Collins with his advanced political theories.
Then others began to join—E. A. Sothern, Benjamin Tick-

nor, William T. Adams, Dr. George B. Loring—journalists, poets, actors, authors.

It was exactly the kind of life he had dreamed about in the long and lonely hours when he had stared through prison bars and wondered if he'd ever again share loud arguments and sharp conversations. Now he had it, and he lived it intensely, as though it might not last—as though it might be snatched away abruptly, and he might find himself thrown back into prison.

He was seldom alone. Night after night—when he wasn't working or lecturing—he would walk the streets of Boston with his friends, or sit with them in his Staniford Street room, smoking and drinking, talking about newcomers in the literary fields and new theories in politics and philosophy, sometimes ripping each other's essays or poems or arguments apart with caustic verbal knives. He enjoyed it, but he reflected that it was a dangerous group for an amateur to approach—a group always ready to stab a man's smugness and make him realize his own mistakes.

And he began also to be a better writer. His work showed the arrival of maturity and balance, as compared to the impetuous and lame sort of poetry he had written before. Young as he was, still he was growing seasoned now, for in the short life that he'd lived he'd experienced more emotional crises and psychological battles than most men twice his age.

He began to write good poetry, the kind of poetry that was to live after him. And when there was a poem to be written, he'd leave his room and his friends and go away by himself to a hotel where nobody could disturb him. He'd stay there alone for hours, not bothered by anything more than the footfall of a waiter in the corridor outside, leaving a pot of coffee and a tray of sandwiches. Sometimes he'd spend a weekend that way, coming out only to go to Mass and then hurrying

back to work again, shaping a new poem and perhaps spend-
ing hours on a choice of phrase. When it was done, he'd take
it straight to the Staniford Street group, hurrying through the
streets on foot or telling his cabdriver to whip up more speed.
And he'd lay it before his critics in the small smoky room
and sit back tugging at his beard nervously and waiting for
their opinion. If they were too harsh, sometimes he'd argue,
or sometimes he'd throw the whole thing away and start
again. And when it was all over—when the praise or the arguments were finished—O'Reilly would go off around the corner to the gymnasium, find a sparring partner, and box until
he could relax in comfortable weariness again.

In that way he wrote two narrative poems that his friends
said were certain to live—"The Dukite Snake" and "The
Amber Whale." For once nobody in the Staniford Street
room made any criticism; instead, they read the lines with
something close to awe. The poems injected a wholly new
note into the world of American poetry—a new note of
strange lands and strange seas and the strange men who had
known them.

When he planned "The Dukite Snake" he thought back to
an old story told by the Bushmen of West Australia, and he
put it into English narrative poetry—the story of a red snake
that kills when its mate is killed, and of the death of David
Sloane's wife and child, and of the mad silent man who then
spent all the rest of his life wandering through the Bush on
the hunt for Dukite snakes.

> . . . So I stayed by his side that night and, save
> One heart-cutting cry, he uttered no sound—
> O God! that wail—like the wail of a hound!
>
> 'Tis six long years since I heard that cry,
> But 'twill ring in my ears till the day I die.

Since that fearful night no one has heard
Poor David Sloane utter sound or word.

You have seen him today how he always goes:
He's been given that suit of convict's clothes
By some prison officer. On his back
You noticed a load like a peddler's pack?
Well, that's what he lives for: when reason went,
Still memory lived, for his days are spent
In searching for Dukites; and year by year
That bundle of skins is growing. 'Tis clear
That the Lord out of evil some good still takes;
For he's clearing this Bush of the Dukite snakes.

It was long, dramatic, colorful, terrible, and fantastic. And
it was cheered by the ones who first heard it on a rainy night
in Staniford Street. It was published first in the Boston *Jour-
nal,* and it told of someone new who had come to American
letters.

Then he wrote "The Amber Whale." For that poem,
O'Reilly reached into the songs and yarns and tales he had
heard during his months aboard the *Gazelle.* He remembered
the old whalemen's fascination with ambergris, and their
stories of giant whales in the warm southern seas—whales
that were seen and pursued but never caught—whales so rich
in ambergris that it had changed even their color and their
substance. And he remembered one yarn about the whaleboat crew that finally had harpooned such a creature and had
been towed miles away from their bark far out on the lonely
seas, and had been cursed by their own greed—and how, finally, all but one had died . . .

. . . And its selfish crew were cursed that night. Next day
we saw no sail,

But the wind and the sea were rising. Still, we held to
    the drifting whale—
And a dead whale drifts to windward, going farther away
    from the ship,
Without water, or bread, or courage to pray with heart
    or lip
That had planned and spoken the treachery. The wind
    blew into a gale,
And it screamed like mocking laughter round our boat
    and the Amber Whale.

That night fell dark on the starving crew, and a hurricane
    blew next day;
Then we cut the line, and we cursed the prize as it drifted
    fast away,
As if some power under the waves were towing it out of
    sight;
And there we were, without help or hope, dreading the
    coming night.

Like "The Dukite Snake," it was long and dramatic and
exciting. O'Reilly sent it to the New York *Tribune,* and
Horace Greeley published it. And again American poetry
readers were stirred with the realization that here was something unusual, a strange and compelling voice, new to American letters.

Greeley particularly was impressed by the poem, and he
made a point of finding out more about the author. He liked
what he found. And so a short time after that Boyle O'Reilly
opened a letter from New York and sat in his Staniford Street
room and whistled softly at the size of the salary Horace
Greeley was offering him to join the staff of the *Tribune.*

It was tempting. But so was Boston. O'Reilly held the letter thoughtfully that night as he looked out over the city
from his high room and wondered what decision to make. He

didn't wonder long. He smelled the scent of coffee and tea and tar drifting up through the darkness from the water front. He saw the shadows of hills in the distance, and thought of the men who had fought there and died on the slopes to help build a new nation. He thought of his work, with the realization that Boston was the literary and cultural center of the whole wide land, and that Boston had taken him in and was giving him a name. He thought of his friends— the ones who boxed with him and walked with him over Beacon Hill and argued with him in the taverns. And he thought of Boston as a swelling center of Irish Catholic life in America, and he realized that if ever he moved to another city he'd still have to reach back to Boston to feel the heart-beat of his own people.

There was too much at hand; he couldn't leave. Boston was his city—not New York or Chicago or any other place in the land.

And besides—and he had known all the time that it would come to this—there was Mary Murphy to think about. He smiled as he thought of her, and he looked out through the darkness and across the river toward the lights of Charlestown where she lived. He had not known her long, but it was long enough to know that he loved her and would marry her if he could. He remembered the strange way he had met her. . . .

In Boston, at that time, there was a youth magazine called *The Young Crusader*. It was edited by the Rev. William Byrne, who later became Vicar General of Boston. It always arrived at the *Pilot,* where it was read for the sake of seeing if it contained anything from one edition to the next that was worth a mention in the newspaper's columns.

O'Reilly read it with that in mind one afternoon in 1870, and he found himself reading over again one beautifully written short story. He looked back for the author's name. It was signed "Agnes Smiley." He felt that he'd like to meet her, so he picked up his hat and walked out to call on Father Byrne. And by the time he returned to Staniford Street that night he'd obtained both a name and an introduction. "Agnes Smiley," he'd learned, was a pen name used by a Mary Murphy of Charlestown.

He liked Mary for being delicate, fragile, warmhearted, and for her sharp sensitivity and her bright sense of humor. Her father, John, had come over from County Fermanagh and was dead; her mother, Jane Smiley, had come from Donegal. He liked Mary's pride in her Irish heritage, a pride as strong as his own. He liked her for being forthright and honest. And when he told her one night that he loved her, she said, "Yes, John, I love you, too." They planned to marry as soon as he could raise a few dollars.

So no letter from Horace Greeley or anyone else was going to disturb his life in Boston, O'Reilly knew; he thought about that, looking out across the night to Charlestown, and he made his decision never to leave for a home in another place, for Boston was wholly his home now and he and Mary could never be so happy anywhere else.

He was delighted, though, to find that when he showed Greeley's letter at the *Pilot* nobody was surprised. Instead, Patrick Donahoe promoted him and raised his salary, to compensate for refusing Greeley's offer. After that there was no reason to wait. The wedding announcement appeared in the *Pilot* on August 24, 1872:

> Married, on Thursday, August 15, the Feast of the Assumption, in St. Mary's Church, Charlestown, by Rev. George A. Hamilton, Mr. John Boyle O'Reilly, of Boston, to Miss Mary Murphy, of Charlestown.

They took a wedding trip through Maine and New Hampshire, and again he was captivated by the beauty and grandeur of the land where he had chosen to live. The rocks of the Maine coast, the leaping white surf, the tall rich pines, and then the rugged granite mountains of New Hampshire and the thick forestlands and the small villages that nestled in the valleys and along the banks of the streams. He and Mary returned to a home of their own on Winthrop Street in Charlestown, but for as long as they could they clung to a hope of someday going back to the north country and learning to know it better.

The thought of Horace Greeley's letter and the opportunities that might have been his in New York never again disturbed O'Reilly's mind. A letter to his aunt Crissy two years later showed how content he was with the choice he had made:

> The *Pilot* Editorial Rooms
> September 7, 1874.

My Dear Aunt Crissy:

It was like listening to you and looking at you to read your kind letter. It has made me so happy and yet so sad that I do not know which feeling is uppermost. *I know* you were pleased to see my poor book; but what would my own dear patient mother have felt when she saw me winning praise from men?

Thank God! I have her picture—the girls and Edward were kind enough to send it to me—and I have it grandly framed and hung in our parlor. My little Mollie loves to kiss it, and I can only allow her to kiss the frame for fear of injuring the picture.

Mary loves to look at it as much as I do, and she loves you, dear Aunt, from your one or two letters. Please write her a letter as soon as you can. She is getting strong again, from the birth of our *second* baby—our Eliza Boyle O'Reilly.

Is it not strangely touching to see this new generation *with the old names*—springing up in a new land, and cherishing as traditions all that we knew as facts?

Somehow I feel as old as you and Uncle James. It seems so long since I was a boy that I really do not, cannot, accept young men or their ways of thinking.

It gives me the sincerest pleasure to know that Uncle James is doing so well. He has a good bookkeeper when he has you; but I am sure he knows that God has blessed him with that greatest of all blessings—a good wife.

Willy's good fortune is as dear to me as if he were my own brother. I always knew he would be a clever chemist, and I am sure he is. Please God, sometime, when the Government lets me, I shall walk into his shop and ask for a bottle of medicine. He would never know the bearded man with streaks of gray, from the thoughtless boy he knew long ago. Nobody in England would know me but *you*. You could see the Boyle in me.

It will please you, I know, to know just how I am doing. I inclose a lot of extracts from the leading papers of America, which will show you that I do not lack literary reputation.

My position in Boston—which is the chief city in this country for literature and general culture—is quite good. I am chief editor of the *Pilot*—which is the most influential Catholic paper in America, probably in the world. My salary is $3,000 a year (2 pounds a day); $4,000 next year. Besides, I write when I please for the leading magazines and literary papers—which also adds to my income.

Of course $3,000 a year does not represent its equivalent in English money in England. Everything is sold at a higher rate here. However, Mary, who is a wonderful manager, has saved a few thousand dollars (I give her all the money) and we are prepared for a rainy day.

My health is excellent. I have just returned from a vacation, which I spent in the glorious southern states of Maryland and Virginia. I visited Baltimore and Washington, and had an invitation to stay with the President of the Jesuit University of Georgetown.

I do not know what you think of America, Aunt, but it

may surprise you to hear that the cities here are far greater and grander than those in the Old World, always excepting London for size, of course. Washington is the most magnificent city I ever saw.

But what do you care for America! Give my love to all, and believe me, dear Aunt, to be,

Always your affectionate nephew,
John Boyle O'Reilly

So, he told himself, the decision to remain in Boston paid off in contentment and, probably, in a swifter rise to prominence. For even with Horace Greeley's backing and New York's varied opportunities, Boyle O'Reilly knew the night he read Greeley's letter that he never could find anywhere else the unique circumstances and advantages that were his in Boston. Still, it was flattering to be invited.

His daughter Mollie was born on May 18, 1873; Eliza Boyle on July 25, 1874. There were to be two others—Agnes Smiley on May 19, 1877, and Blanid on June 18, 1880.

And there was to be sadness, too, for Mary Murphy O'Reilly—the delicate Mary O'Reilly—was to become an invalid. Meanwhile, there was a poem of Boyle O'Reilly's, with Mary in his mind:

A WHITE ROSE

The red rose whispers of passion
    And the white rose breathes of love;
Oh, the red rose is a falcon,
    And the white rose is a dove.

But I send you a cream-white rosebud
    With a flush on its petal tips;
For the love that is purest and sweetest
    Has a kiss of desire on the lips.

26. JOURNALIST'S CREED

THAT YEAR—the year of his marriage—Boyle O'Reilly exposed publicly, for the world to see, his feelings toward the free press of America and its relationship to the challenge of brotherhood. He did it at an affair that left him and thousands of other Bostonians alternately stunned and stimulated, flattened and fascinated, speechless with wonder yet groping for adjectives. He remarked at the time that he didn't think he'd ever get over it.

It was the great International Music Festival of 1872, catalogued by some as an incomparable artistic triumph and by others as an elephantine fiasco of size and noise.

It was planned and staged by a Boston merchant, Eben Jordan, and a Boston-Irish promoter, Patrick Sarsfield Gilmore.

O'Reilly watched it take shape with respect and with misgivings—respect for the imagination of anyone who could envision such a fantastic project, and misgivings about what might happen when the festival hit its climax.

What actually did happen, he noted later, was that the earth of Boston shook and the buildings trembled and the world of music was jarred with a shock it might never again experience. The promoters had built a gigantic coliseum for their show. Singers and musicians came from all over the world. Johann Strauss brought an orchestra from Austria and started the city waltzing. The "Kaiser's Own" cornet quartet arrived from Germany. The Garde Republicaine Band came on from Paris. London sent the Grenadier Guards Band. Dublin sent the Irish Band. America tossed in a one-thousand-piece orchestra and a twenty-thousand-voice glee club. President Grant arrived with his silk topper and his private whisky stock.

And for the climax, O'Reilly and his friends watched Gilmore direct an orchestra of one thousand instruments and heard a chorus of twenty-three thousand voices sing the Anvil Chorus from *Il Trovatore,* while one hundred Boston firemen hammered out the rhythm on one hundred anvils. This was followed by "The Star-Spangled Banner," using all the instruments and voices on hand, embellished by one hundred artillery cannon and the clanging of church bells and chimes from every steeple in the city.

O'Reilly recovered from the impact, reflecting that no other country but America could have staged such a performance, regardless of whether it was good or bad. He'd leave that for the music critics to decide. Meanwhile, he had a job to do that night, appearing as Boston's outstanding Irish journalist at a testimonial banquet for the visiting Irish Band. He walked across the city to the banquet hall with his ears still ringing and his senses still a little confused.

There was no confusion in his mind or in his heart, though, when he was called upon that night, and was cheered to his feet, to respond to a banquet toast for the American press. He looked at the crowd of Irish people assembled there in the hall, enjoying the freedom and privileges of a new home in a young nation, and he thought back to other Irish people who were not so fortunate, and to what a free press could mean in the reshaping of their lives.

"To me, at times," he told his listeners, when finally the applause had stilled, "the daily newspaper has an interest almost pathetic.

"Very often we read the biography of a man who was born, lived, worked, and died, and we put the book on our shelves out of respect for his memory.

"But the newspaper is a biography of something greater than a man. It is the biography of a *Day*. It is a photograph, of twenty-four hours' length, of the mysterious river of time that is sweeping past us forever. And yet we take our year's newspapers—which contain more tales of sorrow and suffering, and joy and success, and ambition and defeat, and villainy and virtue, than the greatest book ever written—and we give them to the girl to light the fire.

"It is a strange fact," he went on, "that nobody prizes a newspaper for its abstract value until it is about a century out of date. It would seem that newspapers are like wine: the older they are, the more valuable.

"If we go into a library piled with books, old and new, we may find it hard to select one to suit our taste. But let a man lay his hand on a newspaper of a hundred years ago, with its stained yellow pages and its old-fashioned type, and he is interested at once. He sits down and reads it all through, advertisements and news and editorials—only, fortunately for the people of olden times, there were very few editorials written then.

"And why does he do this? Because he recognizes the true nature of the newspaper.

"He sees in the yellow paper and the small page what he probably fails to see in his splendidly printed daily or weekly newspaper of today. He realizes as he reads that the newspaper is indeed the truest biography of a day. Its paragraphs and articles are a mosaic of men's daily actions; and his heart feels the touch of the wonderful human sympathy that makes us brethren of the men of all climes and all ages."

O'Reilly paused briefly, and then went on to tell them of one of Boston's early great newspaper editors—of John Burke, who had been forced to flee from Ireland because of his republicanism and his friendship with Napper Tandy, and of how some seventy-six years back he had printed Boston's first daily newspaper. And they stirred with hope and courage as he quoted what John Burke had once written and said in that newspaper:

" 'I call you fellow citizens! For I, too, am a citizen of these States. From the moment a stranger puts his foot on the soil of America, his fetters are rent to pieces, and the scales of servitude which he had contracted under European tyrannies fall off.

" 'He becomes a free man. And though civil regulations may refuse him the immediate exercise of his right, he is virtually a citizen. He resigns his prejudices on the threshold of the temple of liberty. They are melted down in the great crucible of public opinion.

" 'This I take to be the way in which all men are affected when they enter these States.

" 'That I am so will be little doubted when it is known how much I am indebted to their liberality. I shall give better proof of it than words. There is nothing that I would not resign for your service but my gratitude and love of liberty.' "

The banquet crowd sat silent and tense, as O'Reilly halted briefly. Then he went on, to speak for himself:

"Those words were written seventy-six years ago by an Irishman, and although men of our race—and of the religious belief of our majority—have lived down many prejudices and many injustices since then, there still remains a mountain to be removed by us and our descendants.

"With the help of an enlightened and unprejudiced press we can succeed where our forerunners failed. . . ."

And he was thinking along much those same lines months later, when he sat at a table in a private room at the Parker House and looked at the faces of some thirty other men present.

It was late on a Saturday afternoon in mid-December, and these men had come together from all the Boston papers—from the *Globe,* the *Traveler,* the *Herald,* and the *Post,* and O'Reilly from the *Pilot.* They were the men he worked with, the men he liked, and he had found that in their company there was never a thought of any difference in religion or social station or family origin or politics. They were all on the same plane—as newspapermen. And he thought, watching them and waiting to speak, how much good might be done for brotherhood and tolerance if they could band together with a few chosen men from other fields and spread some of their easy fellowship beyond the borders of their own profession.

There was already the Boston Press Club, of course, but what he had in mind was something more embracing—something that would not be confined either by professional limits or dedicated crusades—something that would take the feeling of this Parker House meeting and extend it to others who would understand and appreciate it. The idea stayed in his mind as he toyed with a spoon and listened to the flow of words going on around him.

He looked up at the guest of honor, the man for whom the reception was being held. It was Henry M. Stanley, the reporter who had gone on a mission from the front door of a New York newspaper to the inner depths of the African jungle, and had completed his assignment in a way that had made all newspapermen proud of their calling.

He caught Stanley's eye and smiled. Stanley smiled back nervously. Ill at ease, O'Reilly remarked to himself. He liked that about Stanley—that the man could still feel stage fright, although his name now was known around the world.

He started guiltily, as he heard his own name mentioned. Here he'd been daydreaming, and he was supposed to be on his feet giving the official address of welcome. He got up in his place and bowed to a burst of applause, and went into his tribute to newspaper work as a whole—particularly when it produced men such as Henry Stanley:

". . . a man, a young man, trained only as all of us present have been trained—and yet who had been able to lead an expedition into the heart of Africa, and succeed where the Old World, with all its resources, had failed."

That evening, when the reception had ended, he took Stanley along as his guest, and joined half a dozen other reporters in the tavern room of Billy Park's Hotel, down the narrow alleyway of Central Court. The idea that had caught his imagination at the Parker House table was still moving around in his mind. He brought it into the open over a dinner of lobster and ale, and it caught on immediately.

So that night the Papyrus Club was born—started on a career that was to make it one of the most successful clubs in the history of the city. Ben Woolf of the *Globe* gave the club its name. Its purpose, as explained in the newspapers, was "organizing the leading writers of the daily, weekly, and periodical press of the city in a club, for the purpose of promoting better acquaintance, one with another, and affording headquarters to which gentlemen of reputation in literature and art may be invited while on visits to Boston."

Its early roster held all the names of the group that had spent so many nights together in the Staniford Street room. And it quickly expanded to include others—Thomas Bailey Aldrich, William Dean Howells, George M. Towle, Francis Underwood. And as soon as he could, O'Reilly expanded it still further to take in members who were not necessarily from the fields of literature and art, but who shared the belief that men were born to get along with each other and not to be kept apart by the barriers of prejudice. It became a great club; in time, under O'Reilly as its president, it reached its greatest brilliance.

But meanwhile, that same year, the *Pilot* was hit by the first of a series of blows that were to threaten it with ruin for a time and then, indirectly, lead it along a changed course to a new plane of success.

The first blow came on November 9, the night of the Great Boston Fire. The flames that night leaped wildly out of control. They rode on the wings of an autumn wind. They roared through the richest blocks of Boston's downtown business area, sending walls toppling, roofs crashing. Alleys and streets became swirling channels of flames and sparks and wind-borne embers. Building after building fell into smoking ruin.

O'Reilly stood with his wife Mary beside him, and he watched the spreading sea of flames in despair, and he wondered if there'd be anything left of the *Pilot* rooms when the blaze finally exhausted itself. There wasn't. The *Pilot's* big new five-story granite building on Franklin Street had become a gutted, blackened wreck.

So the paper moved into new quarters in a building on Cornhill. And eleven days later that, too, burned to the ground.

The *Pilot* moved again, this time to a building on Washington Street. And a few months later, on the thirtieth of May, fire wrecked it for the third time.

They moved into temporary quarters again, and O'Reilly wrote the paper's protest for the next edition:

When a fire comes to Boston nowadays, it comes looking round all the corners for its old friend the *Pilot*. It is evident that the fire has a rare appreciation of a good newspaper and a good companion to pass a brilliant hour. . . .

Nevertheless, we do not want to appear too lighthearted on this occasion; it might lead people to think that a fire is not of much account anyway.

Of course we are used to being burnt out, and it does not affect *us* much after the first mouthful of smoke and cinders.

But when it comes to three times in seven months, we protest. We are not salamanders. The oldest phoenix of them all would get sick of such a gaudy dissipation.

For the remainder of our lives in Boston, we want the fire to let us severely alone.

A short time after that Patrick Donahoe called O'Reilly and admitted that he was nearly wiped out. Three blows in a row had ruined his stock and had been more than his insurance could handle. He sat with O'Reilly while the ashes were still warm, and they shared a bottle of whisky and he explained that the best he could possibly do would be to struggle along for a couple of years and try to pay off a few debts.

"It's this way," he said. "My loss runs to $350,000. The *Pilot's* readers are trying to help—some of them who haven't paid a bill in fifteen years have come in with cash in their hands, others are paying their subscriptions for ten years in advance. But it won't be enough. Sooner or later I'll have to quit.

"You're the man who should take it over. I'll hang on for a while. You go out and see what you can raise for backing. When the time comes that I have to sell, you should be the one to buy. And perhaps someday—with the help of God—I can come back in again as a partner."

O'Reilly felt the challenge of the idea. He talked it over with Mary that same night, and they agreed to try it—if they could find a partner. So O'Reilly put on his hat and went across the city to call on Boston's Archbishop John J. Williams.

Donahoe managed to hang on until February 1876, then the load became too much for him to carry. Soon after that the *Pilot* announced its own transfer with a promise to settle all accounts:

> The Most Rev. Archbishop Williams and Mr. O'Reilly, the future proprietors, hope to be able to prevent this terrible loss from falling too heavily on the poor people. With continued success for the *Pilot,* the purchasers intend to pay the depositors every dollar on their books.

O'Reilly called his staff together that day and repeated what he had said at the banquet to the Irish Band almost four years earlier—that there was a mountain of work to be done, but that an enlightened and unprejudiced press could succeed in doing it—and that the *Pilot* would remain a front runner in that field of journalism.

"Someday, with God's help," he told them, "we'll get back to Franklin Street where we belong. But no matter where we publish, this is the way we'll publish—by fighting every wrong until we win, then forgetting the quarrel and saying something kind about our opponent at the first opportunity.

"And for as long as we stay in business, remember this: Never do anything as a journalist that you would not do as a gentleman. Keep that in mind always, and we can't help but succeed."

27. CRUISE OF THE "CATALPA"

THERE STILL WERE MEN imprisoned in the Australian jungle—brave men who had served in uniform in Dublin, who had helped to plan the Army uprising that never came, who had known O'Reilly in those days. And in the year before he took over the *Pilot*, O'Reilly joined a plot to free those men and bring them to Boston.

Some years earlier, in 1870, Britain had given conditional pardon to the political convicts in Australia who had been civilians when they were arrested. They were turned loose and abandoned at the open prison gate and left to shift for themselves. At about that same time Britain had granted pardons to a group of Fenian prisoners in Ireland. Among them were John Devoy, O'Donovan Rossa, John Flood, Thomas Clarke Luby, O'Meagher Condon, and John O'Leary. They sailed together for America, and landed in New York.

But six men who had served with O'Reilly in the Dublin garrison were still wearing chains in Fremantle. They were Thomas Hassett, James Darragh, Martin Hogan, Michael Harrington, Robert Cranston, and James Wilson. All had been betrayed originally by the Army informer, Patrick Foley of the Fifth Dragoons. All were serving life sentences. And now, without warning, the plan for setting them free was being laid before O'Reilly.

He sat with Devoy at a corner table in Marliave's Restaurant in Boston, drinking red wine slowly and nodding at the story of the escape plot. He thought back briefly to other nights at other tables with Devoy—in Barclay's and Hoey's and Pilsworth's—and of all that had happened since those days. He thought of what was still happening to Tom Hassett and the others in Australia.

"We need your help," Devoy said. He studied his cigar soberly for a moment. "The letters I've had from those men —they'd break your heart. Maybe you've had them, too. Anyhow, I saved mine and last year I took them all to a Clan-na-Gael convention in Baltimore and I read them from the floor and I pleaded for help for those men. John, believe me, I saw tears on more than one cheek when I'd finished. The letters themselves told the story—and I was put on a committee with John Goff, Patrick Mahon, Jim Reynolds, and John Talbot —a committee to plan a rescue.

"John Breslin is over here, and he's in the thing with us. He and Tom Desmond—remember Tom?—they're sailing to Australia to work at that end. We need your help at this end in planning and putting the thing together. You know the situation at the prison. We don't. We need your knowledge of the place."

"I'll help," said O'Reilly. "But what are the plans right now?"

Devoy poured more wine into the glasses. "They're fantastic. Yet they may work. Thousands of Irishmen have got to be in on the plot, in order to help raise the money. We'll need, maybe, $25,000—maybe a little more. We've got to gamble on keeping this a secret for at least a year, even with thousands of men in on it—a secret from the British, of course.

"We're going to buy a ship, John. We're going to buy a ship and man her with rugged Irish sailors who aren't afraid of a fight. Then we're going to sail to West Australia and take those men right out of their chains by force if we have to. If we win, they'll get freedom, and British prestige will get a bad kick in the face and every Irishman in the world will feel new strength."

"And if you lose?" O'Reilly asked.

"If we lose, we'll hang—for we're not leaving Australia without those six men."

O'Reilly felt his nerves begin to tighten with excitement. It was the kind of plot he liked. His eyes brightened as he thought it over, and he considered the slim chance of success that it held but the great chance of Irish glory. His mind turned back to his voyage on the *Gazelle,* when he and Henry Hathaway had talked about doing much the same thing.

"I'm in," he said quietly.

Devoy reached across the table and grabbed his hand.

"But I'd like to change the plans a little," O'Reilly went on. "Not much—just enough to make them safer."

"In what way?"

"First, this way. Don't just arm a ship and go charging straight for Australia with your guns blazing. Do it in a way that won't cause anyone to suspect what's going on."

Devoy shrugged. "How do we do that?"

"Easy," O'Reilly told him. "We'll go calling on Henry Hathaway in New Bedford. He's retired from the sea now, living in the city. He'll help us.

"We'll let him in on the plot. Henry's safe—he won't talk. He'll help us to buy a whaling ship, and to get a skipper we can trust. Then we'll man her with a typical whaling crew— Yankees, Malays, Kanakas, Portuguese. Then let her spend a full year on a real whaling voyage—sailing wherever the skipper wants to go, but always moving a little closer to Australia. On a set day she'll put in at Bunbury or Fremantle for supplies. Her log will be up to date. Nobody could possibly question her, even if anyone suspected.

"Then—break the men free. Make rendezvous with the

whaler and put to sea. There are details to work out, but in general that's the way to do it."

Devoy's face was bright with excitement. "When can we go to New Bedford?"

"Tomorrow. We won't waste another day."

Months later O'Reilly and Devoy stood at the New Bedford water front and watched the bark *Catalpa* put to sea. The departure date was April 29, 1875. In command was Captain George Anthony of Nantucket. He was the only man aboard who knew the real mission of the ship.

Anthony cruised the North Atlantic whaling grounds for several months, slowly moving south, and managed to get one whale. Then it was time to leave the Atlantic, and to start moving along to the other end of the world. On a day in early November he sighted the Canary Islands, cleared the light at Teneriffe, and headed south along the coast of Africa on a schedule that would put him off the west shore of Australia the following March.

Meanwhile, Breslin and Desmond had received detailed instructions from O'Reilly and had sailed from San Francisco in September, bound for Sydney. They arrived there in October and were met by two agents already on the scene, John King and J. Edward Kelly. Within the next few days two more men arrived quietly from Ireland, Denis McCarthy and John Walsh. The plans that had been laid back in Boston were carefully examined and approved.

That completed the shore party. They had several months to wait there before the *Catalpa* would be due. They had some $10,000 for living expenses. They began to lay the setting and make their plans for the day of the escape. Breslin and Desmond were to handle the actual rescue. King and Kelly were to serve as rear guards in case of swift pursuit. Mc-

Carthy and Walsh were to cut strategic telegraph wires as soon as the escape began. With those assignments set, they went to work on the job of getting in touch with the prisoners and arranging the timing. It would take careful handling and a delicate approach.

They left Sydney and traveled to Fremantle separately, and while the others stayed in the background, Breslin began to play the role of a wealthy visitor in Fremantle—a man who signed his name "J. Collins" and who appeared to have plenty of time and money on his hands. "J. Collins" seemed to be interested in learning all he could about the city and the countryside—possibly in investing some of his wealth, if he could find something that would show a conservative profit.

During the next months he came to be a familiar figure in Fremantle. At least once a week, all through the Australian summer, from November to March, "J. Collins" would hire a carriage or a saddle horse and ride out through the town. Sometimes he would go leisurely along the roads that led to the places where the convict gangs were at work. In time he met the British governor of Fremantle. It appeared they were becoming close friends, for the governor often rode with him and occasionally took him on official trips of inspection.

Eventually some of those inspection trips wound up at the Fremantle prison. The governor was quite proud of showing off that place, and he was delighted by Breslin's sharp interest. Once in a while, to show how fairly the prison was run, he even allowed a convict or two to talk with Breslin and to answer questions about the quality of food and the rules of discipline. He knew that no prisoner would dare to say anything that might mean extra punishment.

From time to time Breslin saw the men he had come to rescue, and they saw and recognized him—Cranston em-

ployed as a prison messenger, Hogan painting a building outside the prison wall, Hassett planting potatoes in the outer
prison garden, and the others at their various jobs.

Breslin gave them no sign of recognition. In each case,
though, he saw the first quick flash of excitement in their
eyes. He saw them turn away then, as though wearily indifferent to the appearance of another visitor. And he could imagine the confusion of emotion and thoughts that must be
swirling within them—seeing him there in fine clothes,
watching him chat and joke with the governor, wondering
how he had come so far from Ireland, and knowing in their
hearts that he could be there for only one purpose—to rescue
them somehow and in his own good time. Not one of them
ever endangered the plot by the flick of an eyelash. They'd
waited years for release; they were content to wait a little
longer now, and to trust in Breslin to let them know his plan
and to give them the signal for action when the time came.

The months went by. Then early one April morning Captain Anthony sailed the *Catalpa* into Bunbury harbor for
supplies. He hurried ashore and sent a telegram to "J. Collins" at Fremantle. Breslin rode immediately to Bunbury and
went aboard ship to review the final plans for the escape.
They agreed on a whaleboat rendezvous at the coast of Rockingham, twenty-three miles out of Fremantle. The date was
set for April 17, two weeks away. That was the way O'Reilly
and Hathaway had planned it.

Breslin hastened back to Fremantle then, to arrange for
another prison inspection trip with the governor on the following morning. And that day, as they passed a water-front
prison construction job where Wilson was working alone,
Breslin dropped behind, as he had done on many another
morning. The governor walked on ahead, absently chewing a
cigar.

"Jim." Breslin hissed the name and handed Wilson a note. "Hide it!"

Wilson shoved the paper inside his shirt. "God, John! I wondered when you'd speak!" He was trembling.

"The plan's in the note. Get word to the others. Morning of the seventeenth—nine o'clock—you've got to be working outside the walls!"

"We're all on outside jobs, John. We'll be ready. God bless you!"

Breslin turned abruptly and hurried off to where the governor was waiting for him to catch up. "Seems like a nice fellow, Governor. He tells me he's learning a trade."

"Wilson, there? Yes, he's a good chap. One of those Irish mutineers, though. They're a strange group—always silent and moody, as though they were thinking of something far away."

"Perhaps they are, Governor. Well, it's been a good morning, hasn't it?"

They continued their stroll. Breslin reflected how long the next two weeks were going to seem—but longer still for the six men in the prison. There was nothing to do now but to wait and pray.

The timing of the rescue was perfect. Each move fell into place as though it had been rehearsed a hundred times instead of having sprung untested from a conversation between O'Reilly and Devoy in a Boston restaurant. After breakfast on the day set for the escape the prisoners were marched outside the walls to head for their morning jobs. Cranston, with the freedom of a prison messenger, overtook one chain gang and motioned to Wilson and Harrington. "Orders for those two," he told the guard. "They're to move furniture in the governor's house this morning. I'll take them along."

None of the others had to be released from chains. Darragh

was on an errand for the prison's Protestant chaplain, an assignment that had been easy to arrange. Hassett was moving unguarded toward his potato patch, as he did every morning. Hogan had successfully stalled for time on his paint job, so that it would lap over and leave him unchained at just the right moment. One by one, quietly and unnoticed, they drifted away from their work. Once out of sight of the guards, they ran to the meeting place.

They met on the Rockingham road, just in time to see Breslin and Desmond come speeding around a sharp turn, each whipping a two-horse hitch. Behind them came King and Kelly at a fast gallop. The men leaped for the carriages. Wilson, Cranston, and Harrington jumped in with Desmond. Breslin took the others. They tore off down the Rockingham road in a thunder of hoofbeats. Breslin glanced around just once, and thanked God; there was nobody in sight except King, far back and guarding the rear.

They covered the miles to the beach in ninety minutes and tumbled out and dashed down across the sand. Captain Anthony stood waist deep in the water, shouting for them to hurry, steadying the *Catalpa's* whaleboat in the surf. His strongest oarsmen were ready for action. The prisoners leaped in, and the boat shoved off and headed for the open sea. After a long time, looking back across the waves, they saw the faint figures of a group of mounted police dashing along the shore.

The *Catalpa* lay far out at sea, hidden beyond the curve of the horizon. That had been part of O'Reilly's advice, for to have brought her in and had her standing by for the rescue almost certainly would have stirred up suspicion and would have brought British police boats to the scene. Somebody in authority would have been sure to remember another New Bedford whaler—the *Gazelle*.

And so the whalemen bent to their oars, straining to get far enough out so that the tiny boat wouldn't be noticed from the shore. They rowed for hours; then the wind changed and they raised a small sail for extra speed.

Faintly, at last, like a gray spot on the horizon, they brought the *Catalpa* into sight. But storm clouds had been gathering through the morning, and suddenly a quick squall shrieked in from the west, blotting out the *Catalpa* and turning the sea into a gray-white fury.

When the storm had passed, their mast and sail were gone. The bark was nowhere in sight. They rowed on through the night, heading always farther and farther out, fighting more black squalls. They took turns bailing, hour after hour, as the boat shipped heavy seas.

Shortly after sunrise the next day they sighted the *Catalpa* again. But at almost the same instant their hearts jumped with alarm. A British gunboat, the *Georgette,* had come foaming out of Fremantle during the night to close in on the *Catalpa's* course. To make it worse, a British police boat was angling down from the north and also heading for the whaler.

It was going to be close. So far, the British had not sighted the whaleboat, riding low in the sea. But the *Catalpa* had spotted the whalemen, and was bearing down from the distance under full sail. Captain Anthony had a quick choice to make: to lay to, and hope that neither British vessel would see them, or to defy the British and gamble on a swift run for it and try to reach the *Catalpa* first.

He made a swift decision. "All hands! Pull away! Breslin! help rig a jury sail. Hassett! wave your shirt so they'll know we're coming."

In a matter of minutes the whaleboat was leaping through the waves with wind and oars driving her on. The British were closing in—closing in—and the *Catalpa* held grimly to her course.

Then she was alongside, with the *Georgette* speeding in from starboard and the police boat barely yards away. There wasn't even time to scramble over the *Catalpa's* rail. The bark rolled up with her hooks and falls hanging out over the waves. The whalemen quickly secured their boat fore and aft. The *Catalpa* hoisted the whole works aboard—men and boat together. Anthony leaped out with Breslin behind him and rushed across the deck. He glanced back astern and saw the police boat almost within boarding distance. He turned to Breslin and grinned. "What now, Mister Collins?"

Breslin grinned back. "Put to sea, Captain."

" 'Bout ship! Put to sea!" The captain roared the order.

A bellow of threats came from the police boat. The *Catalpa* heeled over on a sharp turn, plunged her bow into a curling wave, steadied herself, and then headed for open waters at a rising speed that quickly left the police boat far in her wake.

They were challenged only once more. Just at sunrise the next morning the *Georgette* overtook and intercepted the bark by making a lucky guess on a change of course. The gunboat closed in from the seaward side and fired a cannon shot across the *Catalpa's* bow. The British skipper bellowed a warning through his megaphone.

"Heave to, there!"

Captain Anthony, leaning against the rail, saw British troops aboard the gunboat, ready to board with swords and rifles. The only thing to do, he decided, was to try to outbluff them. He grabbed his megaphone and shouted back in a voice of anger and indignation.

"Heave to, you say? What nonsense is this?"

"No nonsense. You have six Crown prisoners on board. We're taking them back to Fremantle."

"I have no prisoners here. We're whaling men."

The shouting back and forth brought all hands on deck except the prisoners. Breslin held them below, armed with pistols and ready to fight for their freedom if they had to. Captain Anthony glanced around at his crew and felt more secure. "Get ready for a battle," he ordered them quietly. They began bringing up pistols and knives.

The two vessels rolled along on the swelling seas, beam to beam, almost within touch.

"Permission to come aboard and search?" came the shouted request from the gunboat.

"No, sir!" Anthony shouted back.

"You are under British laws here. Heave to, or I'll blow your mast out!"

Captain Anthony pointed aloft to his American flag. "I know no British laws. I'm an American whaler!"

"I've telegraphed your government that I'm seizing you by force if necessary!"

Captain Anthony waved him off. "I'm bound for sea, sir. Stand clear. I can't wait any longer!" He turned abruptly, and ordered the *Catalpa* to change course. The water gap widened between the two ships. The *Catalpa's* men were rushing whale lances, harpoons, and rifles to the edge of the rail, in plain view of the men on the *Georgette*.

Another shout from the gunboat. "You have fifteen minutes to surrender, then I'm coming aboard!"

"No, sir!" Anthony roared back. "You are not!"

He swung his megaphone to his own crew. " 'Bout ship! Lively now!"

The *Catalpa* rolled hard and her sails filled. Her bow swung into a line aiming dead amidships at the *Georgette*. She picked up instant speed.

"Steady as she goes!"

The *Georgette* hurriedly turned off course to avoid a ramming. The *Catalpa* plunged by, so close the hulls almost scraped. Anthony stood taut, waiting for the crash of the cannon. But it never came. The gunboat turned slowly back on its original course and then headed off toward Fremantle. The *Catalpa* squared away for the open sea, and quickly began to put the miles between her stern and the coast of Australia.

Captain Anthony pulled a handkerchief from his pocket and wiped it across his face. It came away wet with sweat. He looked around and beckoned to his bosun.

"Tell Mister Breslin and his friends to join me in my cabin. We've earned a crack at a bottle of rum. And pour a ration for all hands—my compliments, on the way they came through."

"Aye, sir. You came through well yourself, sir."

Four months and five days later the *Catalpa* came in through Vineyard Sound with reefed sails and moved gracefully into the port of New Bedford. A crowd of thousands lined the water front to greet her with cheers. Cannon thundered from the hills above the harbor. The ship slid gently alongside a dock. Lines went hissing through the air and struck the bollards. Breslin and his men stood at the rail with tears glistening on their cheeks, looking across to where O'Reilly and Devoy were hurrying toward them, equally and unashamedly weeping.

That next night the city leaders put on a great reception and banquet for everyone who had taken a hand in the affair, from John Breslin to the smallest galley boy. And they shouted for O'Reilly to make the speech of honor. Most of his speech was an oration of praise for Captain Anthony.

"I would go a thousand miles to do honor to the New Bedford whalemen," he said. "And now, especially, to this one. He has done a brave and wonderful thing—taking his life in his hands, defying the gallows and the chain gang to keep faith with the men who placed their trust in him. It's almost beyond belief in our selfish and commonplace time. . . .

"England claims this rescue was a lawless and disgraceful raid. That is not so!

"If these men were criminals, then the rescue would be criminal. But these were political offenders against England alone—not against law or order or religion.

"These men had lain in prison for ten years—with millions of their countrymen asking for their release—imploring England to set them free.

"Had England done so, it would have partially disarmed Ireland. A generous act by England would be reciprocated instantly by millions of the warmest hearts in the world.

"But she is blind, as of old—blind and arrogant and cruel. She would not release the men. She scorned even to give Ireland an answer. She called the prisoners cowardly criminals, not political offenders.

"When the *Catalpa* sailed and was a long time at sea, there were doubts and fears for the safety of the enterprise. They were sure to come.

"But Henry Hathaway said once, and for always, 'The man who promised to do this will keep that promise—or he won't come back from the penal colony.'

"As the anti-slavery men answered when they attacked the Constitution—as England herself once answered in the cause of Poland: 'We have acted from a higher law than your written constitution and treaties—the law of God and humanity!'

"It was in obedience to that supreme law that Captain Anthony rescued the prisoners and pointed his finger at the Stars and Stripes when the English vessel threatened to fire on his ship."

Later that month there was one final gesture of protest from Australia. The superintendent of police of Perth sent to the chief of police of New Bedford the names and descriptions of the six prisoners, along with a covering letter:

> Sir:
>
> I beg to inform you that on the 17th inst. April the imperial convicts named here absconded from the convict settlement at Fremantle in this colony, and escaped from the colony in the American whaling bark *Catalpa*, G. Anthony, master. This bark is from New Bedford, Massachusetts, U. S. A. The convicts were taken from the shore in a whaleboat belonging to the *Catalpa*, manned by Captain Anthony and six of the crew.
>
> I attach a description of each of the absconders, and have to request that you will be good enough to furnish me with any particulars you may be able to gather concerning them.
>
> I have the honor to be, sir,
>
> Your obedient servant,
>
> M. A. Smith, *Supt. of Police*

The letter was acknowledged, filed, and thereafter ignored by New Bedford's chief of police, Henry Hathaway.

28. CRY FROM CAPTIVITY

IT WAS a warm summer night, in the year after the *Catalpa* rescue, but as warm as it was, Boyle O'Reilly nevertheless felt a chill. It wasn't the weather; it was the memory. He sat in his home in Charlestown, feeling restless but helpless. There was something he wanted to do, but there was no way to do it. He wanted to help Tom Chambers and Charles McCarthy, but there was no way he could reach across an ocean and through the impassable iron gates of a British prison and snatch them to freedom. The rescue that had worked so well in Australia wasn't worth even a thought when applied to England.

He sat in his home and felt the summer breeze move softly from the dark harbor below, and somehow he felt guilty that he should be feeling comfort while Chambers and McCarthy were still suffering. He wondered how much longer before they'd be released, wondered if there wasn't something he could do to speed that release. He knew there was not.

It was a quiet night. His daughters were in bed. He looked across the room to where his wife sat reading a book by the oil lamp, with the shine of its pale light bringing out the delicate beauty of her face. She felt him looking at her, and smiled and put the book aside, supposing that he wanted to talk. But it was a night for thinking and remembering, and not for talking.

He got to his feet, crossed to her side, and leaned down and stroked her hair.

"I'm going out for a walk, Mamsie," he told her. "I'll be back early."

And so he wandered up and down the dark streets of

Charlestown, with the memories of Dartmoor and Millbank walking beside him. And sometimes the memories made him shiver a little, even in the warmth of the summer night.

It was a letter from Dublin that had brought it all back to him, and so close to him, on this particular night. The letter was a report of what had been bared in the House of Commons on June 5, when the Nationalist, O'Connor Power, had asked for an inquiry into the treatment of the Fenian political prisoners who were still suffering in their cells—more than ten years after the plot that failed. There were only a few of them left. Power had asked why those few were still being held, when the heart and backbone of their movement had been broken so long ago and when their companions had long since found freedom.

The report from Dublin told of how Power had read to Commons the shocking prison description given to him by a freed political convict, Michael Davitt. O'Reilly remembered Davitt well, and he remembered drinking ale with him in Barclay's and Pilsworth's and the other Dublin houses. He had shuddered for Chambers that night, reading what Davitt had written and what Power had read to the members of Commons.

O'Reilly carried the report with him in his pocket as he walked the quiet streets of Charlestown. After a while he stopped at a small tavern near the edge of the water front and seated himself alone at a table in a corner and laid the report in front of him and read Davitt's account again:

> Corporal Chambers, for five months during which he was in custody before trial, was treated far worse than a convict.
>
> I make every allowance for the prejudice of the members of the court-martial in daily expectation of Fenian disturbances. But having found him guilty of treason, why not shoot him? It would have been mercy itself, compared with

sending him to herd with the common thief and murderer. . . .

"Imprisonment for the term of his natural life," signed by
her most gracious Majesty. So ran his sentence, and he was
removed from the Irish jails, where there is some humanity,
to the English jails, where humanity and the Ten Com-
mandments are set aside. . . .

The prison regulations say that the authorities are to in-
still into the minds of convicts "sound moral and religious
principles." Very nice to read. But if the authorities have
neither moral nor religious principles themselves, how
then?

In June or July, 1868, Chambers received "no grounds" as
an answer to a petition that he had sent to the Secretary of
State, begging to be allowed to attend to his religious obli-
gations, a privilege of which he was deprived by a "moral
and religious" director for six months. At present he is daily
driven in and out of chapel by officers brandishing bludgeons
and shouting like cattle-drovers. Even in chapel he is not
free.

Dozens of times those officers have stripped him naked in
the presence of thieves, and subjected him to insults too
disgusting to describe. He is made to open his clothes five
times a day while an officer feels over his body. He has been
several times separated from other political prisoners—although our being together was within the rules—and forced
to associate with picked ruffians. He has been for six months
in constant contact with lunatics. He has been forced to
mop out filthy dens of dirt with a small piece of rag—to
carry a portable water-closet on the public road and across
the fields for the use of common malefactors.

He has often been sick, but except on a few occasions was
not taken to the hospital.

On one occasion, he was sent to the dungeons for applying
for relief after he had met with a severe hurt by falling from
the gangway of a building.

Last year, while he was laid up with rheumatism, they kept him for 16 days on 10 ounces of food daily, and two months on half diet, and then put him out of the hospital far worse than when he was taken in.

He is weekly forced to act as charwoman to a lot of very dirty creatures.

He has had punishment diet (16 ounces of bread and water), penal class diet, and dungeons—dark, cold, wet, and dirty—in abundance. A smile, a movement of the lips—aye, even a glance of the eye—is often condemned as a crime in Dartmoor. . . .

Worthy sons of worthy sires, who shot down the poor prisoners of war here! Their scattered bones were collected, and " 'Tis good to die for one's country" written over them.

When Chambers' sentence of imprisonment is brought to a close, no fine epitaph shall mark his murdered bones.

Nevertheless, the only difference between the French and American prisoners and him is that while they were shot down, he will be slowly tortured to death.

Well, there it was. Nothing had changed since the days when he, too, had worked in the drains and the boneshed. And as he walked back sadly to his home that night, O'Reilly thought how useless it was to try to attack the system through Commons. Nothing would come of a thousand letters such as Davitt's—or appeals like Power's—nothing, except to win the brief chance now and then to let the world know what went on behind the walls of British prisons. But there would be no changes. He was convinced of that. Men such as Chambers and McCarthy would be released at the exact hour the Crown felt so inclined, and it would not be an instant sooner if the scorn of the whole civilized world were to be focused on the scene.

Some six months later O'Reilly heard directly from Chambers, but in a way that swelled his contempt for the Crown's

whole penal system. They had allowed Chambers to fill in
five words on the blank lines of a printed form letter. That
was all he was permitted to write. It read:

> Woking Prison, England
> November 29, 1877

> Dear *Friend*—I was transferred from *Dartmoor* on the
> 26th inst., and am now in this prison; I am in *worse* health,
> and if I do not forfeit the privilege I shall be allowed to
> write a longer letter afterward, *and then* receive one from
> you in reply.

> T. Chambers

But at least it was word that Chambers still lived. And
then, too, since they had moved him from Dartmoor, it might
be that they were planning soon to release him. If so, then
he might need a word of encouragement, to let him know
that he had not been wholly forgotten on the outside and that
there were still friends who cared what happened to him.

With that in mind, O'Reilly wrote him a Christmas letter
and covered it with a special appeal to the governor of Wok-
ing Prison:

> Sir: I respectfully beg that this letter be handed to the
> person to whom it is addressed. His health may be affected
> by despondency which a friendly message may arrest or dis-
> pel. I have tried to avoid breaking your rules or discipline.

> Respectfully,
> J. B. O'Reilly

And he wrote a tender letter to Tom Chambers, scarcely
expecting that it would be delivered but praying that it
might be. After all, he told himself, surely the Crown could
be lenient in the Christmas season.

Boston, U. S. A.
December 22, 1877

John Boyle O'Reilly
to
Corporal Thomas Chambers, 61st Foot; in prison.

My Dear Old Friend: I cannot go to my home tonight without writing to you and actually saying the words, "May you have a happy Christmas, dear boy," as happy as you may have in your sad surroundings.

Your last letter was more a grief to me than a pleasure. I see your familiar hand in only five hearty words. I am glad, however, that the prison authorities allowed you to have my letter. I feared that it would go the unknown road of many previous ones.

Eleven years ago—and what a long lifetime it seems—we were both young and enthusiastic boys, and I am impressed today, somehow, with the vast changes worked on men by time. You in your prison, and I in the world, have both equally changed.

When ten more years have passed, we shall both look back with pleasure—yes, as sure as you live, old friend—at the dark shadow. When your time comes, as it surely will before long, the revulsion of feeling will in itself be so deep a joy that whole years of suffering will be swallowed up.

I grieve to hear of your declining health. Dear Tom, a stout heart keeps a man healthy. Bear up. Remember you have a hearty welcome in the home of one friend—I might say of very many—and now, at the eleventh hour, do not despond nor sink. You must come to us, rugged and strong. Come a boy, to begin the world anew, and to work out your manly way in the New World.

I know that if I were to write news it would break the prison rules and nullify my letter, and I must confine myself to mere words. But believe me, there is a heart behind every sentence.

I do not believe you will be long a prisoner, but, long or short, husband your health for the time of delivery. When you write me, I trust in God you will tell me you are gaining strength. I wish I might write you a newspaper full.

O'Reilly had guessed right. The transfer from Dartmoor had been the first step toward release. And two weeks later, at the *Pilot* office, he received the cabled news that both McCarthy and Chambers had been freed. Then—some days later—another cable: McCarthy had died, almost at the very gates of prison. The years of suffering and torture had been too much. He had died while reaching out for the wife he could scarcely remember and for the children who had grown into strangers.

O'Reilly wept long and bitterly that night—wept by himself, for there was no one in the world with whom he could share his feelings, not even his wife with all of his love for her. He walked alone for hours, through the dark wintry streets and along the cold water front, and he wept as he walked. A soft, quiet snow began falling, and he was grateful, for it seemed to close him away from the rest of Boston and the rest of the world. That was the way he wanted it for those hours. McCarthy was dead, and certainly if prison life had left him that weak, then the best that Chambers could hope for was to live out his remaining time in agony, as a helpless invalid.

But Chambers had written and would be waiting to hear from him. And so after a while he wrote:

I shall not weary you with many words just now. Welcome, my dear, dear old fellow—welcome a thousand times. You mention a long letter you wrote me in November. I never received it, or any other *real* letter from you during the eight years that I have written to you. When you have time to sit down and write me at length, do so.

McCarthy's death was a great shock to me. God rest the poor murdered old fellow.

I sent you a book the other day. I shall publish another in a month or so and shall send that also. Tell me precisely how you are situated and what you propose doing.

I beg of you to avoid the kindly meant demonstrations in your honor, either at home or here, should you come here. It is frothy excitement; there is nothing of it left after a few weeks. It has a good moral effect, perhaps, but the same effect can be secured in another way. You will have to look around now for the means of earning a good livelihood. Pardon my prosaic suggestions, Tom, but I have seen so many men lionized that I have learned to fear the effect on them and to regret it on behalf of those who make the noise.

Should you decide to come to America, come straight to me. I will put a stouter chain on you than ever you saw in Dartmoor.

But somehow he knew as he mailed the letter that Tom Chambers would never be a whole man again, and that whatever years were left to him would be spent in suffering. He wrote a poem about that, and gave it the title "Released." He wrote:

> Haggard and broken and seared with pain,
>   They seek the remembered friends and places;
> Men shuddering turn, and gaze again
>   At the deep-drawn lines on their altered faces.
>
> She offers a bribe—Ah, God above!
>   Behold the price of the desecration:
> The hearts she has tortured for Irish love
>   She brings as a bribe to the Irish nation!
>
> We know her—our Sister! Come on the storm!
>   God send it soon and sudden upon her:
> The race she has scattered and sought to deform
>   Shall laugh as she drinks the black dishonor.

V

STABILITY

(1870–1890)

What shall we mourn? For the prostrate tree that sheltered the
    young green wood?
For the fallen cliff that fronted the sea, and guarded the fields
    from the flood?
For the eagle that died in the tempest, afar from its eyrie's brood?
From "Wendell Phillips."

29. CREATED EQUAL

THE FENIAN MOVEMENT had become a sick and feeble thing. From his editorial desk in Boston, Boyle O'Reilly watched it going through its last pathetic pangs. He felt a little sad, for it was like the death of a brave dream, and a man with the heart of a poet likes to see a brave dream stay alive.

He understood, though, that there was no way for Fenianism to have gone on living. The men who might have kept it alive in Ireland were long since gone from that country, herded into the prisons or forced to flee to other lands. And in America, it had been crippled by misguided Irish enthusiasts who never understood its idealism.

In O'Reilly's mind, it died just about a year before McCarthy and Chambers were released from prison. In his mind it came to an end on February 7, 1877, when the news came out of New York that John O'Mahony had died there, sick and hungry, penniless and neglected—O'Mahony who had fled Ireland in 1848 and had founded the Fenian Brotherhood in America in 1860 and had served for years as its "Head Center."

O'Reilly felt respect and admiration for what O'Mahony had tried to do. Also, he felt contempt for the Irish who at one time or another had followed O'Mahony with their cheers and later had spread the whispered slander that the man had promoted Fenianism only to put money into his own pockets.

With O'Mahony's death, O'Reilly felt something had died that might have been great and good for Ireland; and that its downfall had been quickened by the whisperings of the very men it had tried to help. And feeling that way, when the news came out of New York, he wrote a parting tribute to O'Mahony and published it in the *Pilot* to offset the slanderous tale about the man's motives.

He wrote:

> If any man who made this charge had met John O'Mahony in New York for the past seven years, he would have begged the old man's pardon.
>
> A tall, gaunt figure—the mere framework of a mighty man; a large lusterless face, with deep-sunken, introverted eyes; faded, lightish hair, worn long to the shoulders; an overcoat always buttoned, as if to hide the ravages of wear and tear on the inner garments; something of this, and something too of gentleness and knightlihood, not easily described, were in the awkward and slow-moving figure, with melancholy and abstracted gaze, so well known to the Irishmen of New York as John O'Mahony, the Head Center.
>
> Leaving aside the faults and failures of Fenianism for the sake of its honest and sacrificial patriotism, and for the sake of poor John O'Mahony, whose whole life was a sacrifice, we say that this man's existence and work, though both were darkened by disappointment, were on the whole of good service to Ireland.
>
> Unquestionably the movement of 1865–66 kindled the dead wood of Irish nationalism. There was sore need of a torch and a hand to fire the stubble. There was actual danger of national death in Ireland.
>
> The new generation had been brought up under a system of apparent lenity, and educated in "national schools" cunningly designed to make Irish children West Britons.
>
> It may be that no patriotic light from above, no open political teaching could avert the danger. Be that as it may, the light came from below—it was carried in secret through the country, from town to town, by James Stephens. The peasant

and mechanic lit their lamps at the sacrificial flame—and carried it years after, in loving care, though it scorched them to the bone, in English dungeons. O'Mahony organized Fenianism on this continent. And all of him that was in it was pure and devoted and good.

The life of a good and pure man—a life held in his hand and daily offered up with pagan simplicity for one unselfish object—for his country—can never do that country aught but good. We do not think he was a great man; we never thought him a wise man. But that he was a faithful and un-flinching son and servant and slave to Ireland, no one who knew him will deny above his grave.

God send more men as lovable and unselfish as he! A gen-tleman born and bred, he chose to live in poverty, putting all things aside that might interfere with his dream of a free Ireland.

O'Reilly felt, as he wrote that piece, that he was saying farewell to a part of his life that had slipped away and gone beyond reach. He was an American now. He was no longer an Irishman except in the sense that he would always love Ireland and hope for a free Ireland, and do what he could to make that hope a reality. But as an American, his horizon had widened. As an American, he was concerned with the prob-lems and troubles of America. The cause of Irish independ-ence—while he knew it would be important to him all through his life—was only one of several issues that con-cerned him. The center of his life lay in Boston now, and not in Dublin. When he thought of men living together in broth-erhood, he thought of them as Americans.

Looking back, years later, he wondered a little about when the change had come—about when Ireland had begun to re-cede and America had moved forward and taken first place in his thoughts. He supposed it had been a slow change that had begun when he first began to grasp the enormous problems of intolerance and hate and bigotry that would have to be solved before America could live up to the glorious ideals that had been written down for her by the founders. But he wondered just when it had begun.

There had been that time, some years gone by, when an Indian had murdered an Army officer in Oregon, and angry editorial columns up and down the land had been screaming for the white men to give the savages a blood bath they would remember. So far as he knew, he had been the only editor to write anything about the Indians' side of the quarrel:

> We have too much and too old a sympathy with people badly governed to join in this shameful cry for Modoc blood. We grant that they have committed murder, and that they are unstable, treacherous, and dangerous. Who would not be so, with the robberies and outrages of generations boiling in their blood? If they are ignorant and debased, they cannot be cured by corn whisky and firearms. And these are the only mission books they have received from our government or our settlers.

Yes, somewhere in there the change had been under way. Not that it mattered just when, or how gradually, it had taken place.

And there had been the Jews, too. That was a problem that had nagged and worried him, watching the growth in America of the same prejudice and intolerance that had dogged the Jewish people in their endless generations of wandering. He remembered the time the publication *American Hebrew* had challenged its Christian critics with three questions, in a hunt for the basic reasons for bitterness against the Jewish race. And he remembered that he had published his own answer, which was in a way an admission that he had no answer:

I cannot find of my own experience the reason for prejudice against the Jews as a race.

I do not believe that the cause of this prejudice is the religious instruction in Christian schools, because the most
prejudiced are the least religious or Christian. Part of the
prejudice is inherited from less intelligent times; part comes
from the exclusiveness of the Jews as a race; and the largest
part from the marvelous success of the Jewish race in business.

In this country, I think, the anti-Jewish prejudice is not
at all religious. From personal experience, I should say it
was wholly racial and commercial.

It has been my fortune to know, long and intimately, several Jewish families in Boston and New York, and many individual Jews during my lifetime. Their standard of conduct
is the same as Christians', but their standard of home life
and all its relations is the highest in the world. I know three
men who are my ideals of mercantile honor, integrity, and
business character; one is a Christian and two are Jews.

I do not know how to dispel the anti-Jewish prejudice
except by expressing my own respect, honor, and affection
for the greatest race—taking its vicissitudes and its achieve-
ments, its number and its glories—that ever existed.

Writing such pieces, he knew, had made his name unpopu-
lar in some homes. But nevertheless, he had to write them
because they dealt with American problems and he was now
an American. And he would have written them anyway because they dealt with the brotherhood of man, and because
man needed instruction in brotherhood—needed it badly.

But of all America's problems, it was the plight of the Negro that bothered O'Reilly most and stirred him most. He
sought out the great Abolitionist, Wendell Phillips, and became his close friend, and stood beside him on the lecture
platform and upheld him in the editorial columns in defense

of the Negro and in defiance of anyone who would try to hold
the race down to a level of hopeless servitude. O'Reilly felt, in
that respect, that even Boston was not yet up to understanding the great work Phillips was doing in teaching that all
men—black and white alike—are equal in the eyes of God.
As he said once in 1883, in a letter to the Scranton *Republican:*

> Boston is a great city. Any day you can meet great men on
> its streets. . . . I saw Mr. Emerson and his daughter, who
> was always beside him, come into a horse-car that was rather
> crowded. There was probably not a soul on the car who did
> not know him. And it is sweet to remember the face of the
> great old philosopher and poet as he looked up and met the
> loving and respectful eyes around him. . . .
>
> And Oliver Wendell Holmes—every Bostonian knows
> him. The wise, the witty, the many-ideaed philosopher,
> poet, physician, novelist, essayist, and professor, but best of
> all, the kind, the warm heart. . . .
>
> Much as I love Boston, I am glad I was not born in it, for
> then I could not brag of it to strangers—at least not with
> good taste. Being foreign-born, I can—and I do. . . .
>
> Boston deserves good things, but Wendell Phillips is too
> good for Boston just yet. The city will grow to him in time.
> But to this day, he is like an orange given to a baby—Boston
> can only taste the rind of him. . . .
>
> From his first speech in Faneuil Hall, forty-six years ago,
> to this day, Wendell Phillips has never struck a note dis-
> cordant with the rights and interests of the people. And,
> mind you, he was born and bred a class man, an aristocrat.
> He had the position, the personal attributes, that bind men
> to the higher life and delightful intercourse of the reserved
> and select. All distinction was his. . . .
>
> But if one begins to quote from Wendell Phillips's
> speeches it becomes a kind of intoxication and must be
> abandoned.

His friendship with Phillips encouraged him to speak out more and more vigorously on the Negro problem. And he fought the anti-Negro bigots on two fronts—by challenging them directly, and also by going straight to the Negroes themselves and telling them to defend their rights.

The response he received ranged from the sneering hot-tempered indignation of the intolerants to the endless gratitude of the people he championed and the applause of men such as Phillips—men, O'Reilly reflected, who were at least two generations ahead of the social system that held them back. He wrote:

> The destiny of the colored American is one of the big problems to be worked out in the life of this Republic. The day is fast coming when this man's claim cannot be answered by a jest or a sneer.
>
> The colored American of today may not be equal to his position as an enfranchised man. He has still about him something of the easy submission and confessed inferiority of a race held long in ignorance and bondage.
>
> But this man's children and grandchildren are coming, and they are receiving the same education in the same schools as the white man's children. In all things material before God and man, *they* will feel that they are the white man's equal.
>
> They are growing above the prejudice, *even before the prejudice dies*. And herein is the opening of the problem.

The colored people of Boston read what he had written, and they wondered. They began to speak O'Reilly's name in the slum sections where they lived and in the kitchens where they worked and in the cramped little churches where they met to sing spirituals.

They sent his words along to the colored people of other cities, and O'Reilly was talked about in New York and then in Charleston and then in Atlanta. He knew about it, and felt that he was helping the country in a way, and paying back part of what he owed for his freedom.

Late in 1885 a group of Negroes went to him at the *Pilot* and asked him to be their speaker at a mass meeting of colored men in Faneuil Hall—to talk about the principles of civil rights and human freedoms that were so much a part of the old building's history. He liked the idea. And so he stood on the platform in front of them on a December night—almost the only white man in the hall—and met them with a direct frankness that almost frightened them. He understood why some of them were nervous, for in the recent memories of many of them it would have been worth their necks to be caught listening to such words.

He said:

"I think it is as wicked and unreasonable to discriminate against a man because of the color of his skin as it would be because of the color of his hair. He is no more responsible for one than for the other—and one is no more significant than the other.

"I don't care whether you vote the Republican or Democratic ticket, but I know that if I were a colored man I should use parties as I would a club—to break down prejudices against my people.

"If my children were not allowed into Northern schools—if I myself were not allowed into Northern hotels—I would change my party and my politics every day until I changed and wiped out that outrage."

He gave them something to think about in sorrow:

"I was in Tennessee last spring, and when I got out of the cars at Nashville I saw a sign over the door of an apartment— 'Colored People's Waiting Room.'

"I went into it and found a wretched, poorly furnished room, crowded with men, women, and children. Mothers with little children sat on the unwashed floor. And young men and young women filled the bare, uncomfortable seats that were fastened to the walls.

"Then I went out and found another door—'Waiting Room.' In there were the white people, carefully attended and comfortable. Separate rooms for white men and women, well ventilated and well kept.

"I spent two days in Nashville, and every hour I saw things that made me feel that something was the matter either with God or humanity in the South. And I said going away, 'If ever the colored question comes up again as long as I live, I shall be counted in with the black men.'

"But this disregard for the colored people does not exist only in the South. I know there are many hotels in Boston where, if any one of you were to ask for a room, they would tell you that all the rooms were filled."

And he gave them something to think about with pride:

"No man ever came into the world with a grander opportunity than the American Negro.

"He is like new metal dug out of the mine. He stands at this late day on the threshold of history, with everything to learn and less to unlearn than any civilized man in the world. In his heart still ring the free sounds of the desert. In his mind he carries the traditions of Africa. The songs with which he charms American ears are refrains from the tropical forests, from the great inland seas and rivers of the dark continent.

"At worst, the colored American has only a century or so of degrading civilized tradition and habit to forget and unlearn. His nature has only been injured on the outside by these late circumstances of his existence. Inside he is a new man, fresh from nature—a color lover, an enthusiast, a believer by the heart, a philosopher, a cheerful, natural, good-natured man.

"I believe the colored American to be the kindliest human be-

ing in existence. All the inhumanities of slavery have not made
him cruel or sullen or revengeful. He has all the qualities that
fit him to be a good citizen of any country. He does not worry
his soul today with the fear of next week or next year. He has
feelings and convictions, and he loves to show them. He sees no
reason why he should hide them.

"He will be a great natural expression if he dares to express
the beauty, the color, the harmony of God's world as he sees it
with a Negro's eyes.

"That is the meaning of race distinction—that it should help
us to see God's beauty in the world in various ways."

They called on him again a few months later, when a
group of colored men had been massacred in Mississippi, in
the little town of Carrolton. They called on him to speak out
at an indignation meeting of Boston Negroes, and he went on
an April night to a little church on Phillips Street, and encouraged them to cling to dignity and self-respect as the
guides that would lead them someday to a better way of living.

"You may change the law by politics" [he told them] "but it is
not the law that is going to insult and outrage every colored
American for generations to come.

"You can't cure the conceit of the white people that they are
better than you by politics, nor their ignorance, nor their prejudice, nor their bigotry, nor any of the insolences which they
cherish against their colored fellow citizens.

"Politics tickles the skin of the social order; the disease lies
deep in the internal organs. Social equity is based on justice;
politics change on the opinion of the time.

"The black man's skin will be a mark of social inferiority so
long as white men are conceited, ignorant, unjust, and prejudiced. You cannot legislate these qualities out of the white—
you must steal them out, by teaching, illustration, and example. . . .

"The Negro is the most spiritual of Americans, for he worships with his soul and not with his narrow mind.

"For him, religion is to be believed, accepted, like the very voice of God, and not invented, contrived, reasoned about, shaded, altered, and made fashionably lucrative and marketable, as it is made by too many white Americans.

"I may be pardoned for saying that there is one religion—the Catholic religion—that knows neither race nor class nor color—that offers God unstintedly the riches and glories of this world in architecture, in painting, in marble, and in music and grand ceremony. There is no other way to worship God with the whole soul—though there are many other ways of worshiping him with the intellect at so many dollars an hour, in an economical church, with a hand organ in the gallery, and a careful committee to keep down the expenses.

"The Negro is a new man, a free man, a spiritual man, a hearty man. And he can be a great man if he will avoid modeling himself on the whites. . . .

"The Negro will never take his stand beside or above the white man till he has given the world proof of the truth and beauty and heroism and power that are in his soul. And only by the organs of the soul are these delivered—by self-respect and self-reflection, by philosophy, religion, poetry, art, sacrifice, and love."

Yet even while appealing to the colored people for patience and tolerance and calm thinking, he did not let them forget that there are times when a man must strike a blow in his own defense or give up the battle as hopeless.

He reminded them of that in the columns of the *Pilot* one day in 1890. It was a time when the stories of massacres and lynchings in the South had been mounting, and when finally the climax story told of the savage slaughter of eight Negroes in the South Carolina town of Barnwell. The Boston Negroes appealed to him to write something that would rouse the colored people from despair—and he did.

The black race in the South must face the inevitable, soon or late, and the inevitable is—DEFEND YOURSELF.

If they shrink from this, they will be trampled on with yearly increasing cruelty until they have sunk back from the great height of American freedom to which the war wave carried them. And in the end, even submission will not save them.

On this continent, there is going to be no more slavery. That is settled forever. Not even voluntary slavery will be tolerated.

Therefore, unless the Southern blacks learn to defend their homes, women, and lives, by law first and by manly force in extremity, they will be exterminated like the Tasmanian and Australian blacks.

No race has ever obtained fair play from the Anglo-Saxon without fighting for it, or being ready to fight. The Southern blacks should make no mistake about the issue of the struggle they are in. They are fighting for the existence of their race.

And they cannot fight the Anglo-Saxon by lying down under his feet.

That article brought to O'Reilly a clamor of protest from a hundred different quarters. Letters poured across his desk, accusing him of being a dangerous troublemaker, of stirring the flames that would lead to race riots, and of endangering the lives of blacks and whites alike in the tense regions of the South. It was exactly what he had expected, and what he had hoped to get, for it gave him a chance to wrap up the whole problem of bigotry and oppression in one paragraph.

He did it by replying to the criticism that was printed in another Catholic paper, and which said "It is neither Catholic nor American to rouse the Negroes of the South to open and futile rebellion."

His printed comment was:

True, and the *Pilot* has not done so. We have appealed only to the great Catholic and American principle of resisting wrong and outrage, of protecting life and home and the honor of families by all lawful means, even the extremest, when nothing else remains to be tried. We shall preach this always, for black and white, North and South, please God.

He felt satisfied that night, with the feeling that he was accomplishing some good toward getting men to understand each other and to understand that individual rights were not things to be distributed according to color or religions or family origins. Fenianism was gone, but there were greater fields in which to work. And he was glad that he had been able to reach America and work in them while they were still fresh and fertile.

It never occurred to him that night that a poem he had written fifteen years earlier, about another Irishman, contained the measure of what he was doing. It was the poem "The Nation's Test," written to honor the centenary of Daniel O'Connell's birthday. He had read it before a crowd of 4,000 people in Boston's packed Music Hall—read it from a platform that he shared with Patrick Donahoe, Wendell Phillips, Massachusetts' Governor Gaston, William Lloyd Garrison, Charles Francis Adams, Jr., and others. Within the poem were these lines:

> Races and sects were to him a profanity:
> Hindu, and Negro, and Celt were as one;
> Large as Mankind was his splendid humanity,
> Large in its record the work he has done.

30. THE RICH YEARS

SINCE HE'D BEEN a schoolboy in Drogheda, Boyle O'Reilly had known no formal education. That lack, however, did not stand in the way of academic honors. In 1881 the University of Notre Dame offered him the honorary degree of Doctor of Laws. That same year Dartmouth College offered him honorary membership in Phi Beta Kappa.

Eleven years earlier, in 1870, he had walked down the gangplank of the *Bombay* in Philadelphia and had hurried to the nearest federal court to ask how he could become an American citizen. And now two of the best schools in the country were offering him honor. It made him feel very humble.

On a warm June night, before leaving Boston to go to Notre Dame, he sat late in his office at the *Pilot* and thought back on how kind and generous the country had been to him since the *Bombay* had carried him in to the Philadelphia harbor—how helpful and forgiving his friends had been to him in his early uncertainties and mistakes.

There were his two assistant editors, Katherine Conway and James Jeffrey Roche; he would not have had any success with the *Pilot* except for their help. And certainly it was a success now, with a national reputation and a solid circulation foundation of 40,000. By now it was bringing to America the writings of Oscar Wilde, Douglas Hyde, Katherine Tynan, William Butler Yeats, and their like.

There was, too, young Dan O'Kane, his confidential secretary—poor young Dan who was frail and thin-cheeked and who tired easily, but who was devoted to his work at the *Pilot*. His father John had been that same way before him until he had died just a few years back, almost at his desk, cut off at the age of forty. Without friends such as Roche and the O'Kanes and the rest of the *Pilot* staff, O'Reilly reflected, there would have been little recognition from any source—and certainly no honorary degrees from colleges.

The country, too, had been generous. He had been welcomed on lecture platforms in distant cities—in the far Northwest and the deep South. He had been dined and entertained by state governors, and by cardinals, and by legislators in Washington; and he had found laborers and railroad hands in faraway towns willing to share a sandwich with him in his travels. It was one of the things he liked best about America—that nobody of intelligence was overimpressed by anybody else.

And Boston, of course, had been the most generous of all—had taken him in from the first hour of his arrival, and now seemed proud of the fact that he was being honored in other places. He wondered, idly, why he had joined so many clubs and taken part in other activities in Boston. It wasn't that he had lacked for friends. He supposed the answer might trace back to an unrecognized feeling of lonely insecurity, stemming from the years in the prisons—a feeling that impelled him to grasp at companionship in many places, for fear it might vanish suddenly and leave him with too many memories and nightmares of isolation.

Yes, there had been several clubs. And he had enjoyed them all. He recalled the night he had become president of the Papyrus Club, in 1879, and some of the words of his acceptance speech:

"To be made president of this club would be an honor to any literary man in the country.

"The charm of the Papyrus is that it is essentially an ideal club. The charm of the club to its members will be proportionate to our enthusiasm to work for this ideal; this is our pride.

"Dining, wining, the patronage of millionaires and politicians, the gorgeous service and elaborate style are as vapor and mud beside the beauty of standing up for our independent, brotherly, anti-shoddy, aesthetic, and ideal Papyrus.

"Better for us the expression of a single thought, or the admiration of a high ideal, than all the gold-plated enjoyment of other clubs."

That same year, too, in 1879, he had become president of the Boston Press Club, and he remembered the big dinner the newspapermen of Boston had held that night at Young's Hotel. What was it he had said in his speech?—he tried now to recall the words:

"Our profession changes its units as rapidly as an army in the field. It is a machine always in strong revolution. Its pieces are violently tried, and many drop out unable or unwilling to bear the ceaseless strain. Some of our old members die, and are transported to that Nirvana where the angels are not allowed to use their wings for quills—where there are no nights, and therefore neither morning nor evening papers."

That was part of it, he recalled. But it wasn't what he had been trying to remember. There was another part—yes, now he remembered:

"Ours is the newest and greatest of the professions, involving wider work and heavier responsibilities than any other. For all time to come the freedom and purity of the press are the test of national virtue and independence.

"No writer for the press, however humble, is free from the burden of keeping his purpose high and his integrity white.

"The dignity of communities is largely entrusted to our

keeping. And while we sway in the struggle or relax in the rest hour, we must let no buzzards roost on the public shield in our charge."

That was it. It pleased him to have remembered those words. He hoped he might always live up to them.

And there had been other clubs along the way. Sitting now at his desk in the *Pilot,* with the rooms empty and the gas light reflecting in from the silent street, it was pleasant to look back upon them. There was the Catholic Union of Boston. He had founded that with Thomas Metcalf in 1873—in March—and he was still a member. There was the St. Botolph Club, founded only a year ago and modeled after New York's well-known Century Club. It was a little like the original Papyrus, in the sense that it took in good authors and artists. But it had begun with clubrooms of its own and ample money behind it, rather than at a chop house table. There was that difference.

And, too, there was the Cribb Club—less than a year old, but surely one of his favorites. In fact, he decided it might be that he liked the Cribb Club best of all because of its boxing and rough male competition. They had named it after Tom Cribb, the English fighter, and they had limited its roster to twenty-five active members and one hundred and twenty-five associate members. O'Reilly had been elected to the office of "Second Boss." Already, in the few months it had been meeting, the Cribb Club had built up a long waiting list among Boston's leaders who hoped to be voted into membership and to take part in the boxing tournaments.

It was at a Cribb Club meeting, some time later, when he shifted in his chair with embarrassment and wondered if he could gracefully leave the room while the words of Justin McCarthy, the Irish scholar and patriot, brought an awkward flush to his face:

"Although he is not more than common tall," McCarthy said, "he has the breadth and the thews of a Viking of the days when Olaf Tryggveson dwelt by the Liffey in Dublin town, and wooed and won the fair daughter of an Irish royal house. He excels in all manly arts and accomplishments in a way that we are almost afraid to chronicle, so like a hero of romance that list would make him seem.

"Who among amateurs can ride better, row better, walk better? Above all, who can box better?

"If such a man is red-hot in his enthusiasm for the brawn and biceps of a famous pugilist, it is not with the sham en-thusiasm of the dandies of old Rome who pinched the mus-cles of gladiators with slim feminine fingers. In the society of the physically strong, of the physically skillful, Boyle O'Reilly is among his peers, and if he finds a man stronger or more skillful than himself, it is scarcely wonderful if he accords him his highest admiration.

"It is one of the curious privileges of John Boyle O'Reilly to be universally liked.

"That he should be liked by his own people is only natural. He is one of the brightest ornaments of the Irish race abroad. He lives in exile for his service to his country. He has en-riched its national literature with exquisite prose and yet more exquisite verse. He renders daily service to the national cause. That such a man should be popular with his own coun-trymen is scarcely surprising.

"But Boyle O'Reilly's popularity is not limited to the chil-dren of his own race. Strangers come to Boston—strangers often enough hostile, if not to Ireland, at least to Ireland's national cause and to the men who guide and direct it. The strangers meet John Boyle O'Reilly and they come away with a common tale—enthusiastic praise, unqualified admiration of the exiled Irishman.

"It has happened time and again that travelers in New England, meeting elsewhere, and running over their joint stock of recollections, have each begun to speak with warmth of the man they most admired of all they met—and to find immediately that the name of Boyle O'Reilly was on both their lips.

"Once a very gifted man, a stranger to Boston, met one day a friend, a distinguished Bostonian. Said the stranger to the Bostonian: 'I have just met the most remarkable, the most delightful man in all the world.' Said the Bostonian: 'I know whom you mean—you mean John Boyle O'Reilly.' And the Bostonian was right, of course.

"And there is a Scotch lady living in Boston who tells of walking down a street and seeing two roadway laborers touch their hats to a distinguished-looking man passing by. He returned the courtesy by lifting his own hat and bowing gracefully. And when the gentleman had gone on, and she stopped and asked one of the laborers who he was, the man answered: 'There goes the first gentleman in America—John Boyle O'Reilly, God bless him!' "

That was at the Cribb Club, where they had elected him "Second Boss"—before they got around to changing the title to Vice-President.

Yes, there had been many clubs, with many good friendships and privileges and hours of companionship. He thought back on it all, listening to the ticking of the clock that sounded so loud in the empty editorial room, hearing from the street the clopping of hoofbeats and the joggling of a carriage over the cobblestones, and hearing again in his mind the bits of conversations and speeches and arguments that had sparked his hours with his club companions.

But there had been work, too. Always, from his first night in Boston, there had been work beyond the lectures and the editorials and the newspaper stories. He was thinking of his own creative work; somehow he had always been able to find time for it, even when it meant getting out of bed and being at his desk at sunrise and being back there again at midnight with a day's interruption behind him. It was that important to him, to put down on paper the thoughts and word pictures that came and went in his mind.

That first book of poems, *Songs of the Southern Seas*—he remembered the proud pleasure of holding the first copy when it had been published in Boston. And he remembered, too, the sadness that went with it, for he had dedicated it to Captain Gifford, but it was too late for the *Gazelle's* master to know about it. Just a few weeks earlier Captain Gifford had died on board the *Gazelle* somewhere off the Seychelle Islands, and had been buried at sea in the deep blue waters he had loved so well.

But there had been gaiety as well as sadness in the publishing of poems. He remembered the sardonic glee that had swept through the Papyrus Club when he had pointedly sent two poems to England, to the *Dark Blue Magazine* of Oxford University, and had seen both of them appear in print. And later the laughter at the club when his name had been recognized belatedly by the English publishers, and he had received their cabled suggestion that he not send any more contributions, since they would have to refuse to accept them. By then it didn't matter; he had won his point.

The American critics, in general, had been kind about some of his poems, enthusiastic about others.

The Chicago *Interocean* said of his work: "There is the flow of Scott in his narrative power, and the fire of Macaulay in his trumpet-toned tales of war."

R. H. Stoddart wrote in *Scribner's Monthly:* "William Morris could have spun off verse more fluently, and Longfellow could have imparted to it his usual grace. Still, we are glad it is not from them but from Mr. O'Reilly that we receive it. He is as good a balladist as Walter Thornbury, who is the only other living poet who could have written 'The Old Dragoon's Story.' "

The Boston *Advertiser* said: "The 'Dog Guard' leaves an impression on the mind like Coleridge's 'Ancient Mariner.' "

And the *Atlantic Monthly* praised his "King of the Vasse" very generously: "The Australian scenery, and air, and natural life are everywhere summoned around the story without being forced upon the reader.

"Here, for instance, is a picture at once vivid and intelligible—which is not always the case with the vivid pictures of the word painters. . . .

"The 'Dog Guard' is the next best story in the book—a horrible fact treated with tragic realism and skillfully kept from being merely horrible."

Five years later, in 1878, he had incorporated all the poems in *Songs of the Southern Seas* into a larger volume that was published under the title of *Songs, Legends and Ballads*. The dedication read:

To
My dear Wife
Whose Rare and Loving Judgment Has Been a Standard
I Have Tried to Reach
I Dedicate This Book

That was the year, too, when he began writing in the *Pilot* the serial that was to come out soon in book form as *Moondyne Joe*. It was dedicated "To all who are in prison," and its reception among the critics ran the gamut from high praise to the flat statement, "This is a bad book." He smiled to himself now, thinking back to the editorial battles he had fought in defense of *Moondyne*.

But there it was—and enough reminiscing for one evening. And he got up from his desk and looked fondly about the *Pilot's* editorial rooms, and felt the warm June breeze drift in through the open window and smelled the scents of the city he had grown to love.

He had been a very fortunate man, he told himself. And now it was time to go home and pack his bag, and get ready for the long journey to the Middle West, to the halls of Notre Dame, and then the long journey to the hills of New Hampshire, to the halls of Dartmouth.

He crossed the room to lower the window, and he caught a glimpse of himself in the glass pane as he pulled it down. He rubbed his chin thoughtfully, and then nodded his head. Yes, he was glad he had done it—glad he had shaved off his thick beard. It made him look five years younger—perhaps ten.

31. PROTEST FROM PARLIAMENT

THERE WAS to be one more hot clash between Boyle O'Reilly and the British Crown. In its early rounds, in 1885, it involved the governments of the United States, Canada, and Britain, and it touched off a bitter and caustic debate in the House of Commons. In its closing round, almost four years later, it found President Grover Cleveland angrily demanding the immediate recall of the British minister, while the London *Daily Chronicle* shouted for war.

It began in a simple enough manner. O'Reilly felt quite honored, in December 1884, when he received an invitation from the residents of Ottawa to visit Canada the following St. Patrick's Day and to make the principal speech at a big celebration in honor of the Irish saint. And, incidentally, they added, he could feel assured that he would be safe from arrest.

That he doubted—not because of any distrust of the Irish-Canadians, but because he was convinced that he knew the tenacity of British vindictiveness better than they did—and he felt the British still regarded him as an escaped convict, subject to harsh punishment.

He turned down the Canadians' invitation with regret. And then, out of curiosity, he sent their letter to Washington, to Secretary of State Frelinghuysen, asking if his American citizenship would protect him from arrest in case he did go to Ottawa. And also, since the question had come up, how much protection would he need if he decided to visit Ireland and England as well? Secretary Frelinghuysen relayed the query to the American minister in London, James Russell Lowell.

O'Reilly followed up his move by writing overseas and asking the advice and opinions of the Irish Nationalist members of Parliament. They, in turn, wrote back suggesting that he take the whole matter up with the British Home Secretary, Sir William Harcourt. He did, for by this time the expanding situation had begun to fascinate him and he was tempted to go to Canada just to see what would happen. Would there be a war, he wondered. Or would he simply be shot on sight?

To add another facet to the case, the members of the St. Patrick Society of Montreal decided they wanted O'Reilly to be their St. Patrick's Day speaker even though he had declined the Ottawa invitation. And so they sent a delegation to the government at Ottawa, to get assurances that O'Reilly could visit Canada and still remain a free man. A pledge for O'Reilly's safety was made by Sir John A. Macdonald, Premier of Canada, and Sir Alexander Campbell, minister of justice. They'd be delighted, they said, to have Boyle O'Reilly visit them.

On hearing that news, O'Reilly accepted the Montreal invitation with pleasure. But then the long arm of the British Government reached out from London and stopped the whole business. From the office of the Home Secretary, at Whitehall, dated January 29, 1885, O'Reilly received a terse note:

> Sir: With reference to your letter of the 19th inst., asking permission to visit Canada, England and Ireland, I am directed by the Secretary of State to inform you that he has already received an application to a like effect from the American Minister, to which he has replied that having regard to the circumstances of your case he cannot accede to the request.
>
> I am, sir, your obedient servant,
> Godfrey Lushington

Meanwhile Lord Granville, the British foreign secretary, was reminding Minister Lowell that O'Reilly had been convicted for taking part in the "Fenian Rebellion of 1866," and that therefore the request "cannot safely be granted." On the strength of Granville's stand, a letter from Lowell to Secretary Frelinghuysen wound up with the advice: ". . . that the British Government do not feel justified in allowing Mr. O'Reilly to visit the British Dominions."

In the midst of all this correspondence Thomas Harrington, M.P., an Irish Nationalist, introduced into the British Parliament a petition seeking amnesty for O'Reilly and James Stephens. It was backed up by a speech from the Irish Nationalist, John Sexton, who pointed out that everybody else who had been convicted in the affair of 1866 was now either dead or free, so why hold the ancient grudge against Stephens and O'Reilly?

And that touched off a hot debate in Parliament.

"It cannot be maintained," said Sexton, appealing to the whole House of Commons, "that there was any moral distinction between the case of John Boyle O'Rcilly and the other members of the Army who were tried, convicted, and sentenced at the same time.

"There was, however, one point of difference. Boyle O'Reilly escaped from Australia—under circumstances of daring which attracted general sympathy.

"If by any turn of fortune the home secretary came to be imprisoned himself, would he not make an attempt to escape? He might show as much ingenuity as Boyle O'Reilly, but it is doubtful if he would show as much courage."

Sir William Harcourt yawned in a contemptuous manner. "I should probably be shot by the sentries."

"If Boyle O'Reilly had been shot, we would not be considering his case," Sexton retorted. "The point is that his escape did not increase his guilt.

"I recently had the pleasure of meeting Boyle O'Reilly in Boston. He is a gentleman of very high personal qualities—of the rarest intellectual gifts. He is the co-proprietor, with the Archbishop of Boston, of one of the most important journals in the United States.

"He is one of the most influential men in the state of Massachusetts—one of the most honored citizens in the United States. Long ago he might have occupied a seat in Congress if he could have spared the time from his literary work and the duties of journalism.

"Sir Lyon Playfair—who was the chairman of the Ways and Means Committee of this House—met Boyle O'Reilly in Boston and was so impressed with his personal qualities and gifts that he urged the British Government to extend amnesty —to be generous with its pardon."

Sexton then leaped into a detailed review of the Canadian incident and of Britain's flat refusal to guarantee safe-conduct.

Sir William Harcourt pointedly began to examine a handful of official papers, as though totally disinterested in what was being said.

"The Government committed an error!" Sexton shouted. "Through vindictiveness—because the man nearly twenty years ago escaped from their custody—they refused a request made in true diplomatic form by the minister of a great government with which they claim to be on friendly terms.

"I am forced to describe that as a gross diplomatic error!"

Harcourt smiled and shook his head pityingly.

"The foreign secretary," Sexton went on, "seemed to think the safety of the realm was at stake.

"With the home secretary, it was not a question of the safety of the realm or of moral justification—but merely the word of the right honorable gentleman himself.

"Does the right honorable gentleman know more about Canada than its premier and its minister of justice?"

Harcourt rose to his feet impatiently, as though to dismiss the whole affair. "I could not give him leave to go to Canada."

"But the right honorable gentleman assumed the right to refuse leave!" Sexton protested. "I'm not trying to appeal on behalf of Boyle O'Reilly, for probably he'd never repeat his request—it's doubtful if he would accept permission to go to Canada now, even if it were offered.

"But I protest the course which the home secretary pursued! I point out to the Government that they are exposing themselves to ridicule and contempt throughout America. They are worse than the Bourbons, for they learn nothing!— forget nothing!—forgive nothing!

"I ask the right honorable gentleman, the home secretary, for a decision on the constitutional question."

Sir William stared at him coldly, and replied:

"I had never heard of this O'Reilly before. Certainly his case could not be dealt with in any exceptional way. The case came to me as that of a man who had committed a prison breach. It could only be handled on the ordinary line of prison discipline.

"I did not interfere with the Government of Canada.

"This O'Reilly might be a much respected and distinguished person. But that should not prevent him from being dealt with as any other prisoner."

Another Irish Nationalist, T. P. O'Connor, jumped to his feet. "If the home secretary knew nothing of Boyle O'Reilly, then he would be the only educated man in the world who did not know of the gentleman!

"Mr. O'Reilly is one of the best known, most respected, and most eminent citizens of the United States. And I com-

plain of his being referred to here by the home secretary as
'this O'Reilly.' It's that tone of insolence—of arrogance—of
mean and snobbish contempt—that largely accounts for the
bitterness that colors Irish discussions in this House.

"I complain, too, about the home secretary's use of the
term 'prison breach.' Would the ambassador of the United
States interest himself on behalf of a common burglar?

"This was a diplomatic question in which one great government addressed another great government. The attempt of
the right honorable gentleman to reduce it to the contemptible proportions of a common-law matter was not worthy of
him!

"I say in conclusion that it would do no harm to any
great government to show that it could forget and forgive
offenses."

However, Boyle O'Reilly was no longer interested in the
argument. He sent a cable from Boston, acknowledging the
amnesty petition. The cable said simply:

"Kindly withdraw my name."

The clash was not ended, he assured himself, but it would
have to stay suspended until he could find just the right opportunity for balancing his score with the Crown.

That opportunity came in September 1888.

England and the United States at that time were entangled
in a series of fisheries disputes, with Canada more or less
caught in the middle. In Washington, Secretary of State Bayard had tried to settle the quarrel by pushing a treaty through
the Senate. However, the Republican senators killed it when
they saw that it would have given England almost everything
she had asked for. Next, a two-nation commission was set up
to try to straighten things out. The British commissioner,
Joseph Chamberlain, M.P., almost crippled the work of the
commission at the very start by making a speech that was an

insult to Irish-Americans and a gesture of contempt to Canadians.

O'Reilly watched these things progress toward a climax, and he remembered back more than three years to the Commons debate and the rebuke he had received for seeking permission to enter Canada. This, he decided, was a good time to strike back, not for vindictiveness but just for the sake of puncturing some of the English bombast. Furthermore, President Grover Cleveland was campaigning for re-election. O'Reilly was giving him editorial support in the *Pilot*. If his plan rebounded in just the right way, he reasoned, it might conceivably swing enough votes to keep Cleveland in the White House.

So O'Reilly sent word to Patrick Collins, asking Collins to meet him for chops at Billy Parks'. There he told Collins his plan and they put it into action, gambling that the British minister to Washington would blunder into their trap.

He did.

The minister, Lord Sackville-West, received a letter signed "Charles F. Murchison." It appeared that "Murchison" was a naturalized American, recently a British subject, and that he was a bit confused about the issues in the coming election —such things as the fisheries disputes and the work of the commission and the policies of President Cleveland. And if it wasn't too much trouble, "Murchison" would like the advice of the British minister as to which way to vote.

It wasn't too much trouble at all. Lord Sackville-West sent back a reply without delay:

> Beverly, Mass.
> September 13, 1888
>
> I am in receipt of your letter of the 4th inst. and beg to say that I fully appreciate the difficulty in which you find yourself in casting your vote.

You are probably aware that any political party which openly favored the mother country at the present moment would lose popularity, and that the party in power is aware of this fact. The party, however, is, I believe, still desirous of maintaining friendly relations with Great Britain, and is still as desirous of settling all questions with Canada which have been unfortunately reopened since the rejection of the Treaty by the Republican majority in the Senate and by the President's message to which you alluded.

All allowances must, therefore, be made for the political situation as regards the presidential election thus created.

It is, however, impossible to predict the course which President Cleveland may pursue in the matter of retaliation should he be elected, but there is every reason to believe that, while upholding the position he has taken, he will manifest a spirit of conciliation in dealing with the question, involved in his message. I inclose an article from the New York *Times* of Aug. 22, and remain,

Yours faithfully,
L. S. Sackville-West

O'Reilly immediately put the letter into print.

The shout of angry indignation from the White House could be heard all the way to London. President Cleveland virtually exploded. It was a diplomatic blunder of the worst sort—interfering in domestic politics. And, further, Cleveland knew that to accept British support at the moment would be to commit political suicide. He was outraged. He demanded the immediate recall of Sackville-West. And when London began to hedge and stall for time, hoping the whole affair would blow over, Cleveland summoned Bayard to his desk, gave him an insistent message, and ordered him to get it into the British minister's hands at once. It read:

Your present official situation near this Government is no longer acceptable, and would consequently be detrimental to the good relations between the two powers. I have the further honor, by the direction of the President, to inclose you a letter of safe-conduct through the Territories of the United States.

Sackville-West left the country without delay.

Immediately, then, the shouts of anger began to come from the other side of the ocean. Lord Salisbury, for one, indignantly berated Cleveland's administration for daring—as he put it—to "flip out" a minister of the Crown. The British press in general took up the fight and castigated the United States as "crude—insulting—boorish—ignorant." And in particular, the British press placed the blame squarely on the heads of O'Reilly and Collins.

The *Daily Chronicle* declared:

> If President Cleveland is of the opinion that it consorts with his dignified position to abase himself and his country before the O'Reillys, Collinses, and other Irish demagogues, and to reserve his rudeness for accredited diplomatists of friendly powers, it is not British business to attempt his conversion, but it is our duty to resent the insult put upon us as promptly as it was offered.

That ended the affair.

Cleveland lost his bid for re-election, but only by a small margin, and it was obvious that he had picked up considerable strength by his firm action against Sackville-West.

O'Reilly was satisfied. He had almost kept Cleveland in office. At least he had made a good try.

And he was convinced that Sir William Vernon Harcourt, who had never heard of "this O'Reilly" some three years earlier, certainly had heard of him by now.

He felt that the account was squared.

32. IN GOD'S CARE

MARY O'REILLY found it hard to get to sleep that Saturday night in August. The whole week had been hot and sultry. She was worried about what the hard work and humid weather might be doing to John. That day, when he'd come down to Hull on the midafternoon boat from Boston, he'd been looking tired and drawn. She kept telling him, these days, that he needed a long vacation—that here was this fine big summer house, with the broad waters of the Atlantic almost at the front steps—a good place for relaxing.

She remembered how much he had looked forward to summer visits when he'd bought the property eleven years ago, back in 1879. The place had seemed rickety when they'd first moved in. It was one of the oldest houses in the country—1644, they'd told her, built by the Rev. Marmaduke Matthews and later the home of various British Colonial officers. But the location itself had been promising, well out on the Nantasket neck and just a pleasant cruise from Boston on the harbor boat. So they'd bought it and had torn down Marmaduke Matthews' decaying home and had built a new house on the site. They'd put in a sundial in the yard, along with several old shipwreck relics, and they'd worked together planting flowers and making designs with shells from the beach.

It had been fun, and it was fun now to have the family together for the summer. But John never seemed to have time to enjoy it except for short weekends. And now that she was an invalid herself, the time between those weekends seemed very long. She knew it was important that he do his work, but for his own sake she wished he'd take a rest. Here it was the ninth of August and he should be ready to stay at Hull for the rest of the summer, but instead he was planning more speeches and more editorials for the next week. Twice in the past few weeks, his friends had told her, John had collapsed in public. She was worried.

But he wouldn't stop working, and neither would he admit that he felt tired. That afternoon at the boat landing little Blanid had met him with all the enthusiastic gaiety of a ten-year-old, and Mary had heard them laughing and shouting at each other on the way up the road to the house. Well, if he really felt that full of spirit, she supposed, perhaps she was worrying too much. At any rate, she knew he was resting now, in the tower room close to her bedroom, probably reading a book and smoking a cigar and quite content to be with his family again if only for a few hours. It was late, though. Before long she'd have to make sure that he went to bed and didn't stay awake reading all night, as he sometimes did.

As for herself, she couldn't sleep. She had chloral medicine on hand for her insomnia. She had taken as much as she dared, and then she had put it back in the medicine closet. It hadn't helped. But the doctor had warned her not to take too much, even when she couldn't sleep, for it was strong and deceptive and dangerous. Earlier in the night she had asked John to go out and get more medicine to help her sleep, and John had brought the doctor back with him. The doctor had given her another bottle, and had warned her again against the danger of taking too much chloral. Then he'd left something mild in the medicine closet for John to take, in case he, too, couldn't sleep.

At times like this she felt especially sorry that she was an invalid, almost helpless. If she were able to move around freely now, she could go to John's tower room and coax him to take her for a walk in the darkness, and they could go down along the beach and wander by the waves and lie on the sand and watch the stars and talk about poetry. It had been so much fun, in the years when they could do those things together. But now it was all she could do to get from one room to the next. John was patient, though. He was kind to her. And he loved his family—always doing something to help them.

She remembered the time, a year or so ago, when she'd been away on a short trip of her own, and had come home unexpectedly one morning, just before dawn. And instead of finding them all asleep, she'd found the children wide awake and sitting at his feet as he read the last pages of the *Arabian Nights*. He'd gone through the whole book with them at one reading.

She liked his way, too, of pointing out cultural values to the children—not as an impersonal teacher but as a friend. She had saved one of his letters in which he had done that, writing to Agnes and Eliza Boyle when they were in convent school at Elmhurst:

> Boston
> November 19, 1889
>
> Dear Bess and Agnes:
>
> At last I am out of the wood of hard work that has shut me in for two months. . . .
>
> I have never been so busy in all my life as I have been since Mamsie and I came from the mountains. I have literally not had a leisure hour for fifty days.
>
> I long to go to Elmhurst and see you—I wish you and I could go away in my canoe, down a long, sunny, beautiful river, and camp on the banks for weeks and weeks, till we were rested, rested, and had forgotten the busy, noisy cities and all the work and trouble that are out in the world.
>
> I suppose Mollie has sent you the poem I read at Georgetown University. It was well received by the Cardinals and

Bishops, and they were a very grand audience, filling the whole room with their crimson and purple robes.

They were very kind to us in Washington. We saw some great and wonderful things in many cities while away; but we saw one little work by a great man that made us forget everything else—buildings, monuments, bridges, and cities. It was a picture—a little oil painting, eighteen inches square—"L'Angelus," by Millet, which was on exhibition in New York. . . .

You know the picture from the engraving; it is the same size; but the coloring is like the very touch of God Himself in the sweet flushing sunset. Far away on the fields is the church spire. The sun is very low and is not seen; but the most exquisite gentle flush that ever was painted by man touches the bowed head and crossed hands on the breast of the praying woman and the back of the head and shoulders of the man.

It is not a man and woman praying—it is a painted prayer. You can hear the Angelus bell filling the beautiful air; you can see the woman's lips moving; you pray with her.

One looks at the lovely picture with parted lips and hushed breath. And so great is art that *all* who see it feel the same sweet influence. . . .

We could hardly go away from it; and as we did go, we looked at nothing else there. Everything else had lost value. . . . All day and ever since I keep saying at times to Mamsie, "I can see the reddish flush on those French peasants"; and she says, "I can hear the Angelus bell whenever I think of the picture."

And yet the genius who painted this treasure sold it for a few hundred francs. He lived all his life in a little French village. He was not regarded as a great man, and he died very poor. . . .

The children were fortunate, she reflected, to be able to learn their values in such a way—and from such a man. Yes,

especially from such a man. And she was fortunate to have
him for a husband. She liked the way the columnist "Tav-
erner" had written of Boyle O'Reilly in the Boston *Post:*

"He is one whom children would choose for their friend,
women for their lover, and men for their hero."

She remembered, smiling, how that had embarrassed John,
and how he had tried to keep her from reading it. But it was
right. Children did like him; he was a considerate and exciting lover; and men did look to him as a leader.

But he'd been so tired lately—and the nights were so
hot. . . .

She strained her ears to listen, hoping she could hear some
sound from the tower room that would let her know if he
were still awake. It was silent, but that didn't mean he'd gone
to bed. Probably still reading, or perhaps just sitting alone
and remembering some of the strange hours of his strange
life.

She wondered if he would go off on another canoeing trip
in the autumn. He thought that was great sport—the best of
all sports, next to boxing. He'd even written a series of articles about it and had them published in the Boston *Traveler,*
and he'd been as proud of seeing them in print as though
he'd written another novel or another great poem. She
laughed a little to herself, remembering the time he had
started on a canoeing trip toward the headwaters of the Connecticut River. He had sent back a telegram on his first day
out:

"Spilled. Send two double paddles to Holyoke, first express. Don't mention."

Since then he'd canoed the waters of the Merrimac, the
Delaware, the Susquehanna, the Connecticut—even the dark,
wild interior of the Great Dismal Swamp in Virginia, where

he'd sat with Negroes at their campfires and told them of their abilities and their rights and their destiny.

He had told them, for example, "We must not be Irish or African, or black or white. Not in America. We are gathering here, and boiling down here, all the best blood—the blood of the people—not to build up any petty community, but to make the greatest nation and the strongest brotherhood that God ever smiled upon.

"Those of us who came from Ireland—we are done with Ireland, except in the love and hope we and our children have for her. If Ireland were free tomorrow, we'd continue to live here as Americans. We wouldn't go back.

"And you, as Negroes. The Negro strength is in unity now, and it must continue so until white pride and prejudice and ignorance are broken. Then, when that happens, the Negro strength will be in the brotherhood of all Americans. Work always for that day. Never get discouraged."

They had understood him, there in the Dismal Swamp. They had asked him to come back to them and tell them more, and he had promised that someday he would, God willing. He had told Mary all that when he'd returned from the South.

Many times in those past years she'd been able to go along with him on his trips—canoeing, beachcombing, rattling from city to city in smoky trains to see how other people were living and to learn what they were thinking. It had been fun always, with him.

She thought for a moment, now, that she heard a noise from the tower room, and she listened closely. There was nothing. She thought it might have been John walking back and forth in his shortened pace—three steps this way, three steps that, in the habit he had formed in the cramped prison cells and had never been able to abandon. But there was nothing. No sound at all.

Yes, it was a good life with him. And if only she could get over her illness, she would make it a happier life than ever he'd had in the past. It was fun living with him, for he lived the way he worked—always on the deadline, lest he miss something that might turn up at the last instant. And it had been fun seeing him get into arguments and hearing him declare himself. Like the time he had argued about religion with that friend from the West, and had written a letter for the friend to find when he returned home:

> Puritan you, with your condemnation of the great old art-loving, human, music-breathing, color-raising, spiritual, mystical, symbolical Catholic Church! A great, loving, generous heart will never find peace and comfort and field of labor except within her unstatistical, sun-like, benevolent motherhood.
>
> I am a Catholic just as I am a dweller on the planet, and a lover of yellow sunlight, and flowers in the grass, and the sound of birds. Man never made anything so like God's work as the magnificent, sacrificial, devotional faith of the hoary but young Catholic Church.
>
> There is no other church; they are all just way stations.

He'd be going to Mass in the morning without her. She missed the pleasure of being with him on Sunday mornings these days, but it couldn't be helped. Perhaps someday she'd get better and could go with him again. And in the meantime, it was pleasant to remember all the things that had happened to them together.

"*. . . one whom children would choose for their friend, women for their lover, and men for their hero.*"

Such a fine way to say it!

But if he were going to get to Mass on time in the morning, and not be too sleepy, she'd have to see that he got some sleep now. It was getting much too late—much too late. She'd better go to the tower room and talk to him, but she'd just close her own eyes for a moment or so before making the effort. . . .

Soon she was breathing heavily, fast asleep. It was almost dawn when Mary awoke again. She sat up in bed, startled, taking an instant to collect her thoughts. She thought she'd heard somebody call her name. But the house was silent. She glanced at the clock. It was almost four. Suddenly she was terribly worried about John. She considered calling out for him, but if he were asleep, that would only disturb him and upset his night's rest. No, she'd find out for herself.

Painfully, she managed to get from her bed and slip a robe over her shoulders and make her way to the tower room. There was a light shining under the closed door. He was still awake, then. She tapped on the door and went in. She saw him sitting on a couch, with a book in his hand and a cigar in an ash tray beside him. He looked at her and smiled drowsily.

She crossed to the couch and sat beside him. "John, dear, it's almost sunrise! You haven't had a minute of sleep."

He patted her hand vaguely, uncertainly. "John," she cried, "what's the matter!"

He shook his head. "Nothing, Mamsie dear—nothing's the matter. I couldn't sleep, but I think I can now. I'm very tired."

"John!" She put an arm across his shoulders. "Are you all right? Do you feel ill?"

"I'm all right, Mamsie. I couldn't sleep, but I can now. I'm tired. I'll just lie down here on this couch and go to sleep right away."

She got up, still with her arm around his shoulder, and

eased him down onto the couch. He was terribly drowsy. His face seemed to be growing pallid. She hurried to loosen his clothing. He murmured something, but she couldn't understand what he said.

Suddenly she had a frightening thought.

"John!" She shook him violently, and he roused a bit and half-opened his eyes. "John, listen to me! John! Did you take sleeping medicine? Do you hear me, John!"

"Hmm?—Yes, my love. I took quite a lot. I'll sleep."

"John! Which did you take? Are you sure you took the right one? John—you've got to listen! Did you take my medicine? John!" She cried his name loudly, to bring him back to consciousness.

"Yes, Mamsie—love. I took the medicine. I'll sleep."

She knew then, and the shock was terrible. She screamed again and again. The sound was a wild, desperate cry that rang all through the big house. She heard the sounds of the others, hurrying from their bedrooms, running along the corridors.

"Bess!" she cried. "The doctor, quick! Your father's dying."

She stumbled to the medicine closet, hoping frantically that she was wrong.

The bottles told the story. Boyle O'Reilly had groped in the dark. Her bottle—the strong and dangerous chloral—was almost empty. Boyle O'Reilly's mild sedative was untouched.

She crumpled to the floor in tears. But even in her grief she found her mind darting back to something he had once said to her long ago. His words came back to her now:

"Mamsie, dear—some men think they're too busy to take the time to die. Then God takes care of it for them."

33. HONORED CITIZEN

THE WORDS of sorrow and tribute came from many levels, many places. They came from the White House and from the tarpaper shanty, from the laborer's kitchen and from the Cardinal's study, from broad city streets and from misty swamplands. They kept coming in for weeks.

Perhaps Boyle O'Reilly would have been touched at first, if he could have heard and read the messages. But he would have become uneasy and a little embarrassed as they mounted by the thousands. And probably, after just so long, he would have asked that they be stopped. He would have said that no man deserved such words. But embarrassed or not, he would never have been able to deny the genuine grief and the real shock with which his death affected so many men and women.

Cardinal Gibbons, who was then the head of the Catholic Church in America, called the death "A public calamity—not only a loss to the country, but a loss to the Church and to humanity in general." In New York, statesmen, soldiers, and educators held a big memorial meeting at the Metropolitan Opera House and paid honor to O'Reilly both with letters of sympathy and spoken words—from President William Henry Harrison and a long list of college presidents, senators, governors, and clergymen.

At the O'Reilly home the messages kept arriving in a torrent that seemed to have no slackening. Grover Cleveland, vacationing on Cape Cod, wrote of Boyle O'Reilly as "A strong and able man, entirely devoted to any cause he espoused, unselfish in his activity, true and warm in his friendship, and patriotic in his enthusiasm." Dr. Oliver Wendell Holmes, writing from his home at Beverly Farms, spoke of O'Reilly as "A man of heroic mold and nature; brave, adventurous, patriotic, enthusiastic. We have been proud of him as an adopted citizen, feeling always that his native land could ill spare so noble a son. He was a true and courageous lover of his country and of his fellow men."

And also from the literary world, George Parsons Lathrop hastened to write from New London: "He is a great rock torn out of the foundations of my life. Nothing will ever replace that powerful prop, that magnificent buttress. I wish we could make all the people in the world stand still and think and feel about this rare, great, exquisite-souled man until they should fully comprehend him."

The eulogy, at St. Mary's Church in Charlestown, was given by O'Reilly's close Jesuit friend, the Rev. Robert Fulton. The words were heard by a strange crowd of newspapermen, statesmen, high clergymen, New Bedford whalers, Negro laborers, Irish dynamiters, Boston editors, all sitting as Boyle O'Reilly's friends and with his family. Father Fulton, in his oratory, reached a great climax:

"Has it ever struck you that for the success of our great cause Mother Church greatly needs lay champions? Some such there are in other countries; here there are none, or few.

"Such a champion would need talent, but more would he need orthodoxy, respect for legitimate authority. He should give example in observing the ordinances of religion. His life should be a deduction from her spirit. Such was O'Reilly. . . .

"He was approximating Christ, for such is our Exemplar."

And in a written eulogy, published in a Boston paper, the Protestant clergyman, Rev. H. Price Collier, said:

"If the Almighty should undertake to create a man who

was to be universally popular, no doubt he would create him a Celt. . . .

"John Boyle O'Reilly was a Celt of the very best type, whose friends were in the right and whose enemies—if he had any—were in the wrong; for his friends were all made for him by his real character, and his enemies by mistaken estimates of him."

And so the tributes went, rolling and mounting and pouring in, and finally reaching their biggest public display at a mass meeting in Tremont Temple. There the leaders of Boston truly bared their feelings for Boyle O'Reilly and thousands listened, saddened by his death but glad he had been among them for a while.

And it was at that meeting that Patrick Collins made the finest speech of his career, gave the finest tribute of all to the man who had been his closest friend:

"'For Lycidas is dead ere his prime—and has not left a peer.'
"Even in this solemn hour of public mourning it seems hard to realize that we shall see him no more.
"Men who knew us both will expect from me no eulogy of Boyle O'Reilly. You mourn the journalist, the orator, the poet, the patriot of two peoples—the strong, tender, true, and knightly character. I mourn with you, and I also mourn—alone.
"But after all, the dead speak for themselves. No friend in prose or verse can add a cubit to his stature. No foe, however mendacious, can lessen his fame or the love humanity bears him.
"Yet we owe, not to him but to the living and the future, these manifold expressions of regard—these estimates of his worth. The feverish age needs always teaching.
"Here was a branded outcast some twenty years ago, stranded in a strange land, friendless and penniless; today wept for all over the world where men are free or seeking to be free, for his large

heart went out to all in trouble, and his soul was the soul of a freeman. All he had he gave to humanity, and asked no return.

"Take the lesson of his life to your hearts, young men!—you who are scrambling and wrangling for petty dignities and small honors. This man held no office and had no title. The man was larger than any office, and no title could ennoble him. He was born without an atom of prejudice, and he lived and died without an evil or ungenerous thought.

"He was Irish and American—intensely both, but more than both. The world was his country and mankind was his kin. Often he struck, but he always struck power, never the helpless. He seemed to feel with the dying regicide in *Les Miserables*—'I weep with you for the son of the king, murdered in the temple, but weep with me for the children of the people—they have suffered longest.'

"Numbered and marked and branded. Officially called rebel, traitor, convict, and felon, wherever the red flag floats. Denied the sad privilege of kneeling on the grave of his mother. Thus died this superb citizen of the great Republic.

"But his soul was always free—vain are all mortal interdicts.

"By the banks of that lovely river, where the blood of four nations once commingled, in sight of the monument to the alien victor, hard by the great mysterious Rath, over one sanctified spot dearer than all others to him, where the dew glistened on the softest green, the spirit of O'Reilly hovered, and shook the stillness of the Irish dawn on its journey to the stars."

INDEX